Common Roots
A Framework For Integrated Living Curriculum

Social Studies

Science \ ecology

creative arts

health \ nutrition

language arts

math

gardening

community service

Exploring the Forest with Grandforest Tree

TABLE OF CONTENTS

WINTER 🐾

SPRING 🐦

Preface

For us at Food Works, and for literally hundreds of children, teachers, parents and community members, this *Common Roots™* Guidebook represents far more than a collection of hands-on environmental activities for the young learner. For all of us, this Guide is a roadmap for placing schools back at the center of communities - by providing students with opportunities to address critical concerns in their neighborhoods, towns, surrounding countryside and larger world.

Food Works grew out of our community work attempting to unravel the spiral of hunger, poverty and ecological collapse locally and globally, from rural Vermont to rural Africa.

Through this work, we discovered that the very ways we learn about the endangered world both reflect and recreate that world. In elementary school, for example, we learned to divide up the world into neat categories - Math, Science, Social Studies and so forth. We then applied those same tools in adulthood to divide up the world— Politics, Economics, Environment, etc.— which has led to a patchwork of temporary band-aids rather than sustainable solutions to these endemic problems.

In trying to create a world that nourishes all forms of life, we must from the earliest ages teach ourselves to see the world as an interconnected whole of which we are an integral part. We at Food Works believe the purpose of schooling should be to nurture the natural curiosity, imagination and dreams of all children, in order to re-create a world capable of responding to the diverse spectrum of intellectual, emotional, creative and nutritional needs of all its inhabitants.

Common Roots provides the practical skills enabling our children to more holistically understand and explore the inter-relationships between the natural and human world. Therefore, we at Food Works have dedicated our work to transform the role and responsibility of our schools in order to identify and respond to the food and ecological concerns of our communities in order to create a healthy future.

Joseph Kiefer

Acknowledgements

The *Common Roots*™ framework as a vehicle for re-inventing schools would not have been possible without the desire and enthusiasm of the many teachers, parents and children to change the way we look at the role of our schools.

The Rumney School was the first to offer us a school to pioneer the development of the *Common Roots* framework that included the K-6 Historic Theme Gardens.

The Barnet School hosted our first *Common Roots* graduate course which taught us the critical importance of each teacher owning his or her unique journey for integrated learning. This collaborative relationship continues to grow and bear fruit.

Additionally, we would like to thank all of our new schools and the unique way they have adapted *Common Roots* to meet their needs.

Unquestionably, none of this would have been possible without the dedication and vision of the Food Works collaborative team. The rich insights and personal teaching experiences of JoAnne Dennee, Julia Hand, Carolyn Peduzzi, Elisheva Kaufman, Jack Peduzzi, and Joseph Kiefer have inspired the genesis of *Common Roots*.

The guidance and support of our Board of Directors has been instrumental in sustaining the *Common Roots* vision. Their collective wisdom is a constant source of inspiration and direction.

Most importantly, we would like to acknowledge the many family and foundation funders whose generous support has enabled us to realize our common dream. By believing in our vision and continuing to support this evolving work, this group of friends has become part of our growing Food Works family.

Above all, listening to the voices of children has taught us the timely need to provide meaningful opportunities for them to create a better world.

A Word About *Common Roots*
A Guide to An Integrated, Living Curriculum

Welcome to the Common Roots Guidebooks, a collection of hands-on seasonal projects and activities for the curious child.

The Common Roots Guidebooks have been designed for teachers, parents and community members to create a living curriculum for children which integrates the human and ecological roots of their own community. These K-6 Guidebooks offer hands-on learning activities and projects for children to discover the past, explore the present and build their common future. These adventures are developmentally designed along a 7 year journey that help tell the story of each child's community, from its very first inhabitants (grades K-2) to its local heritage (grades 3-4) to a look to the future (grades 5-6), thereby creating a living curriculum of meaningful activities.

These Guidebooks integrate traditional subjects into each of the projects and activities that build upon each other as the child moves from Kindergarten through Sixth Grade. Social Studies is an integral part of the historic theme gardens - the hub of the Common Roots learning process for each grade level. The Applied Scientific Method is part of every activity. Children marvel at fermentation processes as they bake bread; track the life cycle of seeds; observe the effects of weather, fertilizer, insects and worms in their own gardens; and investigate and analyze sources of local water for pollution. Language arts are acquired as children write garden journals, read recipes or create a community ecology-action newsletter. Math skills are developed through designing a garden, measuring cooking ingredients and graphing changes in ecosystems. Art, music, dance and physical activity are also integrated into the activities to allow children to celebrate seasons and the cultures they are learning about.

Common Roots is an inquiry-based journey for children, guided by their teachers and parents and accompanied by their elders and neighbors. The meaningful hands-on projects and activities nurture children's natural curiosity by providing the opportunity for each child to express their creativity and knowledge in order to answer their own questions. This student-centered approach engages students in the process of learning rather than providing textbook answers to rigid curriculums.

Common Roots provides children with real-life opportunities to develop problem solving skills to research, document and help preserve their fragile environment and disappearing heritage - building a better world for

The Common Roots Journey

tomorrow. The projects and activities climax at the 6th Grade level, but the journey exploring our natural and human world is lifelong.

Put on your pack and come along with us!

Introduction to
Exploring The Forest With Grandforest Tree

"Every season of the year there are things to discover in the forest. Fall is filled with the rustling of squirrels and chipmunks, scurrying through the dry leaves looking for food. Changing leaves turn the forest into a fantastic display of light and color. And though many flocks of birds fly south for the Winter, some will remain if you feed them. Look, too, for signs of animal wanderings on the snowy landscape. In Spring, watch for the explosion of life brought by warming weather.

All the creatures of the forest welcome you to their woodland home. They ask that you take care while visiting, and respect their home as if it were your own."

Grandforest Tree guides children through the forest on an adventure filled with stories, activities, and learning. The guidebook is divided into three sections, each representing the seasons Fall, Winter, and Spring. Each section contains many activities designed to slowly expand a child's knowledge of the forest to encompass an understanding of the inter-relationships of all the forest's inhabitants. As the seasons turn, the child's own place in the natural world also begins to unfold.

Each activity is based on a question or questions that *the child* asks, and then follows through with discoveries that lead to the answers. The activities are presented in such a way that one question leads to another. As well, within each activity is a section entitled "Want To Do More?", which guides the child to a deeper understanding of the world he or she is exploring.

Throughout the activities, traditional curricular studies are entwined. Thus, nature itself becomes the teacher of science, history, art, writing, music, and health. Frequently, a section entitled "Math, Nature's Way" is included in the activity. In this manner, the child receives an education that is relevant, engaging, and makes sense.

The delightful pen and ink illustrations that accompany each story invite color or paints. As you read a story, pass out a copy of the accompanying illustration to each child. Crayons, colored pencils, pastels, or paints will make them come alive! Afterwards, let them draw their own imaginative illustrations.

Should there be any questions, Grandforest Tree is always there to help.

Fall

GRANDFOREST TREE TELLS OF THE FIRST FOREST

This guided journey takes you back to the birth of the first forest. You might like to share this while lying quietly beneath the forest canopy, or against a large rock outcropping covered with moss. Make sure to choose a day that is sunny and warm!

Hello, tree friends. My name is Grandforest Tree, and I am very old and very wise. I'd like to tell you how the forests came to be. You see, it's quite an amazing thing for a forest to grow.

"Long, long ago, in the days of the very first forests, evergreen forests did not mix with forests which dropped their leaves. Each had a different taste for the soil - evergreen favored sweet soils and the leaf droppers preferred sour soil. Each forest kept mostly to its own ways, except two trees in the Northeastern states: the White Pine of Peace and Old Hemlock. They were rather friendly fellows who would take up housekeeping in just about any hospitable forest. Though trees prefer special places for growing and may not have mixed freely back then, all trees belonged to the world family of trees and were cooperative and friendly with each other.

"But before the first forest began, way, way back in time, the Stone People ruled the land. There was no soil, and thus no place to send down roots. Sister Rain alone kept the Stone People company. She kept things refreshed and, from time to time, worked hard to smooth things out. Sister Rain's many guises, especially snow and ice, helped her do her work. Day after day,

year after year, the Stone People and Sister Rain kept things in order.

"One day, however, someone new arrived in the desolate world of the Stone People, the 'One with Courage Beyond Compare'. This fine pioneer, who began to settle on the land of the Stone People, became known as Lichen because he was the only character known to take "a likin'" to the Stone People. You see, although well meaning, the Stone People were rather cold, so most passers-by kept on going. But not Old Lichen! He had ideas of his own. He set out on a quest that took him into every nook and cranny on the Stone People's land.

"Lichen's journey took a long, long time. At first everything looked pretty much the same out there, and it was difficult for Old Lichen to tell where he had been, or where he was going. But one day he had a brilliant idea: by leaving a mark on the Stone People's faces, he could map the path of his journey.

"Eventually, Lichen's crusty, map-like marks appeared everywhere, giving the smooth stone faces a bit of character. Slowly, slowly, the dreary, desolate landscape began to change.

"The Stone People realized that Lichen's work was magical, and that an amazing transformation was occurring right on top of their faces. Indeed, those many-colored crusty markings were doing the work of a Giant! Lichen's map-like crusts were actually cracking and crumbling those Old Stone faces, causing special features to appear.

"Several ages later, Miss Moss passed through the Stone People's Land. She couldn't help but notice the changes that had occurred. Miss Moss was weary of traveling and constantly moving from place to place, so you know what she did? She threw down her pack and settled right into the cracks that Lichen had prepared. This was the first cozy place Miss Moss had found on this planet! Her home was so inviting that it inspired other Mosses to settle down. Soon Miss Moss had the companionship of many Moss People, as whole villages of Moss formed!

"Some time after the Moss villages were established, Fern happened by. Like Miss Moss, Fern had been traveling ever since he could remember. He, too, longed for a pillow to rest his tired feet. He was happily surprised by the soft Moss Villages. 'Come join us!' sang the Moss people. Without hesitation, Fern settled into a cool, green bed.

"Unlike the others, who were short and stout, Fern stood tall, gently waving to the others below. It was a nice arrangement - Fern's fronds kept things cool and breezy, and Moss's softness was a blessing for Fern's feet.

"Well, as you might guess, more and more Fern People rested their weary feet in the cool, green moss. Their jovial nature was welcome in the fine villages. Before long, even the Stone People were singing along with Lichen, Moss and the Fern people. Growing was in, and rock silence was out!

"The bustling in the Stone People's Village was unlike anything they had experienced before - though some had imagined it in their dreams. After much cooperation between the Stone People, Lichen, Moss, and Fern, several generations came into being. And as each generation grew old and spent, it lay itself down in the embrace of the Stone People. After several generations of this activity, the skin of Mother Earth began to form real, living soil! Aside from the lichens, mosses and ferns, new grasses began to grow. What had once been vast stretches of stone became endless meadows. Gradually the meadows invited more and more plants to come live with them, and then animals. The meadows became meadow-thickets, and, eventually, forests.

"The story you just heard took longer than you can imagine and more cooperation than you can dream of. For, you see, Sister Rain, the Daughter of Mother Earth, had been a lone companion to those Old Stone People for thousands and thousands of years! After the Lichen, Moss and Fern people arrived, many millions of years passed before the skin of the earth - the living soil - became deep enough for plants to grow. The transition from meadows to thickets to forests took thousands more years.

"Now, you're probably wondering how an old tree like me might know all this. Well, the Stone People have been passing this story through untold generations of Lichens, Ferns, and

Mosses. When some of the first Tree People breathed in the breath of the Earth, they heard the story from the whispering winds. Since that time, the trees have whispered this and other stories in the winds."

♠ After the journey, open your eyes and move quietly about,silently observing all the parts of the forest that Grandforest talked about. If you are with a group of friends, someone can give an agreed upon signal, such as an owl hoot, to call the group back together after five or ten minutes. Team up with a friend to share something special you discovered.

♠ Can you illustrate Grandforest Tree's story?

TREES FOR LIFE JOURNALS

Journals celebrate all the gifts of the trees - through poems, drawings, seasonal photographs, and preserving leaf specimens. When you make your own journals, you will appreciate all the parts of a tree that go into the making of a book.

You will need:

two thin 8 1/2" x 11" (or larger if desired) cardboard pieces to make the cover

reusable gift wrap, fabric, construction paper, or newspaper to decorate the cover

at least 20 sheets of recycled white paper (clean on one side)

birch bark glue

darning needle and strong quilting or button thread

hole punch

scissors

ruler and pencil

thimble (optional)

(Continued)

To make your own journal:

1) To make a **journal cover,** use recycled cardboard from cereal boxes or corrugated cardboard boxes. Measure and cut two 8" x 11" pieces of cardboard for the front and back cover. If you prefer a bigger journal, measure and cut accordingly.

2) **Decorate the journal covers** with recycled gift wrap, fabric, large easel paper, construction paper, or newspaper. Glue this covering onto the cardboard covers as if wrapping a present.

3) You might enjoy making a **birch bark title plate** for your nature journal. Fallen scraps of birch bark can be collected while hiking. It is important to remember to <u>not peel</u> any bark from standing trees, as this bark, or "skin", provides protection from insects and disease. You can cut shapes from fallen bark with a sharp pair of scissors to form a title plate for your journal cover. Handle the bark gently as it may be brittle. Glue on the bark title plate firmly, then press the covers beneath heavy books to dry.

4) If you use **recycled paper** to fill your journal, glue two used sides together. When the glue is dry, measure and cut the paper to fit inside your journal covers. This will leave you with two clean sides that can be filled with drawings, thoughts, poetry, pressed leaves, or stories.

❧ Depending on the size paper you are working with, you may **assemble your journal** in one of two ways:

If the paper is the <u>same size</u> as the book covers:

1) Make several holes with a hole punch along the front and back cover so that the holes fall in the same place on each cover.

2) Next, punch holes in the paper so that the paper holes exactly match the cover holes.

3) Make a sandwich with the front and back cover, and place the paper filling inside.

4) Stitch together the covers and paper with a darning needle and some yarn, cotton or strong quilting thread.

5) After the book is assembled, make a crisp fold down the front cover next to the holes where the paper and cover were stitched together. This fold will help your journal stay open when you work in it.

If your paper is to be <u>folded in half</u> between the covers:

1) Open the folded paper and neatly place the pages on top of one another.

2) Place the two covers side-by-side on top of the paper filling. You will see a fold in the paper, which marks the place where you will place the book binding.

3) Match up the top, edges, and bottom of the covers with the paper filling.

4) Make a binding from a piece of strong, thick felt or wide, colored tape. Place the book binding on the covers so that the binding fills the gap at the fold and overlaps a half inch or so at the edges of the covers.

5) Glue or tape the binding to the cover.

6) When the glue has completely dried, the folded paper filling may be stitched to the book binding. You might find a thimble helpful for pushing the darning needle through the thick paper filling.

🍂 You might want to include a page inside which gives the date, author's name and a publishing company name, such as Friends of the Forest Publishers.

This journal is wonderful for documenting your memorable experiences, such as picnicking in the shade of a tree, swinging from a tree, being fed by an apple tree, building a tree house, jumping in leaf piles beneath a tree, or finding pine cones and acorns for imaginative play. This book may contain a creative tale as well as poetry, tree rubbings, pressed leaves, drawings and photographs. It can even contain all the discoveries you make!

TO BE A TREE

Find a special tree friend and stand beside it for this exercise. Choose a tree that calls to you, to which you feel drawn. If you like, you can adopt this tree for the year, and return to visit it often.

🐴 Create a **"sensing circle"** around your chosen tree. You can stand alone or join hands in a circle of quiet friends. Observe the light, the shadows, the colors and shapes which appear on the tree. Listen to the silence or to whispers in the air. Listen to the murmurs of the land and the call of nearby animals. Feel the warmth or chill, feel any winds that draw near the tree and move within the circle. Take a deep breath in, then let the deep breath out. Smell the air and earth, which give life to this tree and to you. Drop hands. Feel the anticipation in the air as you prepare to go on a Guided Journey with this tree.

I magine what it would be like to be a tree. Let's go on an imaginary journey and travel deep into the quiet of this tree to learn its secrets. Close your eyes. Let your feet feel like roots, holding you in place. Take some deep breaths. Inhale, exhale, breathe in-n-n and ou-ou-out, in-n-n- and ou-ou-out, like the breath of the tree.

Now raise your arms and stiffen them so they feel like a strong tree limb. Stiffen, stiffen, stiffen your arms - now drop them! And relax. Imagine a soft breeze gently relaxing you just a little bit more. Now stiffen your back, stomach, and legs so they feel like the strong trunk of a tree. Stiffen, stiffen, stiffen them - let go! Now relax. Breathe regularly as you imagine the gentle breeze soothing you a little more. Tense and spread your toes, spread them like roots reaching far out into the earth. Spread, spread, spread those toe roots! Now relax them, and breathe. Gently wiggle your toe roots as they spread out across soil that supports every part of you.

Now pretend you are standing tall with your forest family. Your trunk is stretching up to the sky, your branches are spreading and reaching out wide. Your roots reach deeply into the earth. Feel (or imagine) the warmth of the sun on your leaves. As you receive the life-giving energy of the sun, let it fill you with a deep breath. It fills your leaves, it fills your branches, it fills your trunk, it fills you deep down to your roots.

Your roots and bark, branches and leaves, are filling up with life. Your leaves are making food, clearing the air, creating fresh clean air for all. Reaching deep downward into the earth, your thirsty roots draw up water. They carry it to all parts of you. Then your leaves give some water back to the sky.

Like a guardian of the forest, your branches reach out to protect all. The life in you is reaching out, giving away to all

the others - the trees, the animals, a bird nesting in your
branches, each forest visitor, even the sky. All the earth is
cared for by you, and you are cared for by the earth and sky.
Feel what it is like to be a tree in this caring circle of life.
When you feel ready, you may slowly open your eyes and
look at your new friend, the tree.

Tree Curiosity

In your journal, draw or paint yourself and your chosen tree friend.
Use colors that remind you of how it felt to be a tree. As questions arise
about your chosen tree, record them as well.

ADOPT A TREE

Throughout history, trees and people have always seemed to share a special relationship. Trees have been around since the age of dinosaurs - some of them are the oldest living things on Earth. Over the years, certain trees have taken on special meanings to those who visit them. Choose a tree that you especially like and "adopt" it to discover what an amazing friend a tree can be!

    🌰 Find a special tree to adopt for the year. If no trees are close by, plant a young tree outside - or plant one in a tub inside. Throughout the year, return to your tree to share nature stories, do artwork, have special gatherings, and observe and record seasonal observations in the life of your adopted friend.

    You will probably have some special stories to tell about your friendship and the experiences you have had with your tree. Here are some stories about trees other people have loved.

    ♥ Did you know that Buddha had a special tree friend? Buddha thought the **Bo Tree** to be sacred and often sat in contemplation in its shelter.

    ♥ **Old Sherman** lives in a California forest. Old Sherman is so large that it takes 21 children to join hands around the trunk. Every year this **3500-year old Sequoia** is visited by thousands of school children who enjoy giving it a group hug! If you can get 21 friends to join hands in a circle, you can see just how wide this ancient friend grows.

    ♥ Have you heard about the **Traveler's Tree** on an island in Madagascar? This tree welcomes thirsty travelers with a pint of water cupped at the base of each large fan leaf!

(continued)

♥ **Tree of Peace** is a White Pine tree that several Iroquois nations planted long ago when they joined together in peace. The eagle sits as guardian on top of it, and promises to call out a warning cry any time peace may be threatened.

Want To Do More?

🕊 Take a **"Tree Inventory"** to discover the best loved or famous trees in your neighborhood! Locate historic trees that were planted when your neighborhood was founded, trees that withstood lightning, fire, or the big flood! Locate the oldest tree, the youngest tree, the tallest tree, the widest tree. Find a tree that can hold the most maple buckets, a tree that has been eaten by a pileated woodpecker, or any tree with a special story to tell.

      ❧ Publish and illustrate a **guide** to "Trees We Love In Our Neighborhood".

NATURE NOTES: JOURNAL ENTRIES

Whenever you visit your adopted tree, make an entry in your Tree Journal. Soon it will become a book of magical and wonderful things!

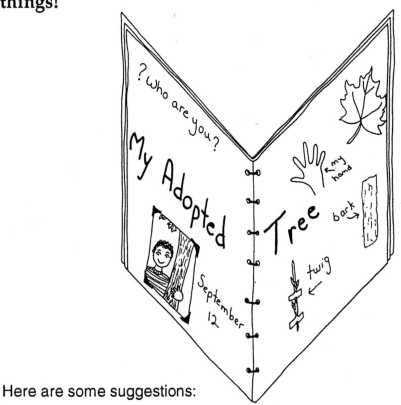

Here are some suggestions:

🍂 **Draw** your adopted tree from season to season. Include homes for other living beings, such as insect holes, woodpecker holes, moss, nests and cocoons.

🍂 **Ask** your tree questions from season to season.

🍂 **Record** your conversations with, and impressions of, Grandforest Tree. Keep track of questions you might like to ask him next time you visit him.

🍂 Each season **take photographs** of yourself and your adopted tree.

Note your growth and compare it to the tree's growth during that season! Write poems to accompany the photos.

🍂 **Laminate a leaf** from your tree or make a **leaf rubbing.** To make rubbings from leaves, rub the side of a crayon over a piece of paper with a leaf beneath it. Like magic, the special characteristics of the leaf will appear! While looking at all your leaf rubbings, appreciate the special characteristics of each leaf. Then outline the leaf, following the pattern on the leaf edges. Is it smooth, toothed, lobed?

🍂 **Trace your hand** on the opposite page from an Autumn leaf sample. Compare the size and shape of the mature leaf to your own hand. Does the leaf resemble a mitten or fingers?

🍂 **Glue a twig** onto a page. Arrange drawn, rubbed or pressed leaves along the twig, just as they appear on the tree. Are the leaves in an opposite pattern? Do they take turns, alternating?

🍂 **Cut a piece of bark**, or a crayon bark rubbing (you can make a bark rubbing the same way you make a leaf rubbing), in the shape of a tree trunk. Glue this bark sample to the page. Is the bark smooth? Does it have a rough feel? Is it speckled? You may also draw the tree's branches as they rise out of the trunk of the tree. Do the branches fan out, create a triangular shape, create a canopy, or reach straight up to the sky?

🍂 You may **make seasonal drawings** of you and your tree hugging one another, swinging together, visiting in your tree house, collecting sap, eating apples, or day dreaming together.

🍂 **Mount pressed leaves** in your Tree Journal that tell the story of the changing seasons. If you want to preserve a leaf in your book, use a decoupage fixative to preserve the leaf and attach it to the page. If you press leaves and place them within clear contact paper, the preserved leaves will last forever, although they may fade over time.

🍂 **Illustrate the tree's gifts** and how we benefit from them. For example, draw leaves decomposing into soil. Show how animals and insects use leaves as food. Create drawings that show humans and animals

gathering or eating fruits or nuts. Draw furnishings made from wood. Don't forget that tree trunks provide shelter for insects, birds and snails. Leaves offer shade. Trees reach out with beauty and friendship.

🍃 **Write a poem, a song, or a story** about your friendship with the tree.

🍃 Make your own **Tree Guidebooks**. Use leaf rubbings, pressed dried leaves, bark rubbings and illustrations of tree shapes, plus descriptions or drawings of each tree's home. You can also illustrate stories about the tree's qualities. Each type of tree can have its own chapter to celebrate all its unique characteristics.

TO KNOW A TREE

Every tree has its own biography! Every family of trees holds its unique leaves and waves it in a particular way. And each tree family enjoys a special habitat that suits it just right. Individual trees carry themselves in a characteristic way. Each has a silhouette and a gesture all its own. By putting all these special features, or clues, together you can really get to "know a tree for life"!

Visit your adopted tree. Look closely at this special friend to discover the story of its life.

❧ Where does it prefer to live?

- Is it in a grove with other trees?
- Alone in a sunny meadow?
- Does it prefer to stand on the edge of a forest, greeting the meadow?
- Does the tree prefer to live near a stream or pond, where it can dip its feet?
- Does it stand high and alone on the hilltop, stretching toward the heavens, catching the light shining down on the Earth?

❧ What is the shape or character of the tree?

- Is it umbrella-shaped, like a sheltering willow?
- It is triangularly shaped, like an evergreen?
- Is it rounded, like a maple?
- Is it fan-shaped, like an elm?
- Take a few minutes to look at it from a distance and compare it to some other tree neighbors. How is it unique?

❧ What can you learn about a tree by feeling it?

- Hug the tree's trunk. Feel the touch of its bark on your cheek and beneath your fingers. Hug the tree again, this time with your eyes closed.
- Can you stand quietly, resting your back on the trunk of the tree as though you were part of the trunk?
- Try stretching your arms around the trunk to feel more like a part of the whole tree.
- Do this quietly, eyes closed, for an entire minute. How do you feel after being part of a tree?
- Can you recreate the shape of the tree with your body?
- How do you feel when you are in this position?
- What are you trying to say to the world with your "tree body"?
- Can you send that feeling right back to the tree?

(continued)

🍂 What do you discover as you explore the bark again, using more of your senses?

- Look at it up close. Does all the bark on the tree, from bottom to top, look the same?
- Can you find some older cracked bark that has split and stretched to grow wider around the trunk?
- Can you find some young, smooth bark?
- What makes this tree's bark special?
- Does this tree's bark seem like the kind of bark that could be useful for making canoes or shelters?
- Do you know that tree bark can range from white, red, silver, gold, to brown, beige, gray and even pink? See if you can find any of these colors of bark on your tree.

🍂 What do the leaves tell us about the tree?

- Each leaf is like a fingerprint and tells the family of its birth. Study the shape of this tree's leaves, then look nearby for other trees in this family.
- Are they smooth, waxy or fuzzy?
- Are they in the shape of a hand? Or mittens? Or do they remind you of feathers?
- Are the edges smooth, jagged, or lobed?

LEAFING AND BUDDING THROUGH THE YEAR

In this activity you can document a year in the life of a leaf! Each week, collect a leaf of the same species. Mount it on a display board and watch what happens during the life of a leaf!

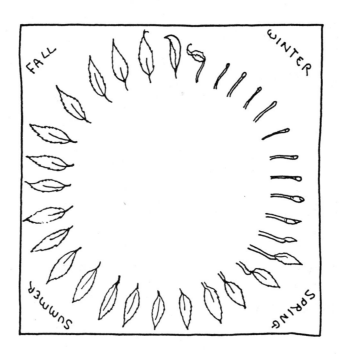

You will need:

large poster board to mount display
markers
leaves, twigs, buds
glue

🌿 Throughout the year, **pick and preserve leaves, buds, and flowers.** Leaves can be picked every week, from Fall to Spring. It will be important to include the bud stages beginning in late Winter, and to follow their development through the flowering stages of early Spring. Press or dry each leaf, flower or bud you pick. Make careful notes of the date each time you pick, press and dry a leaf or blossom.

1) You will need a large poster board to mount your entire display. Organize it in a shape that appeals to you, such as a large circle, a spiral, or as a border around the edges of the poster board. Plan to have a space for 52 specimens, one for each week of the year.

2) You might want to label the dates, illustrate the months and seasons, or add any other interesting information or a running story about your tree. You may also consider including a photo of yourself with your tree in every season. Who's growing in what ways?

3) As you add a leaf to the poster board, you will notice changes in the leaf's size, color, and shape. You may want to note the changes of each season on your poster board as you attach leaves during the cycle of the year.

Want to Do More?

⚜ Start up a **Leaf Exchange Project** with another relative or class in a different part of the country or world! As Leaf Pen Pals, you can exchange interesting information along with the leaves. For example, you might send a Leaf Pen Pal in the West some colorful leaves the class has laminated which show how maple trees change to rainbow colors every Autumn. You might tell how Maple trees are the sap givers of the Spring. You might describe all the activities involved in making syrup from sap. You can even send a taste of maple syrup, describing some of your favorite ways to enjoy it.

Forest Shelter

Can you create an outdoor Ecology Action Research Station (EARS) near the tree you adopt? It can be a rustic lean-to, a permanent shelter, or simply a place to sit (beneath an umbrella, if you must). However you decide to make it, your EARS station will be a busy place this year! It will become a center for caretaking, discovering, imagining and creating special events. It can even become a place where you sit together to envision the future.

🍂 **Stumps, stones, or woven sit-upons** can help you create a circular area, which defines your forest location.

🍂 A **rustic lean-to** may be lashed between two trees. Use sturdy, fallen limbs gathered from the forest floor.

🍂 A **permanent outdoor wooden structure** may be constructed with community assistance.

🍂 A **fire circle** will give your special place a mood of magic and wonder. Gather around the fire circle for a ceremony, some storytelling, a birthday celebration or an evening nature watch. Camp out at the fire circle.

🍂 **Make a sign** for your special place or EARS station that describes your dedication, respect and caretaking responsibilities.

Want to Do More?

🍂 For a community building exercise with some friends, paint a **Circle of Friends Tree Mural.** Paint a large tree on a large sheet of paper or an old sheet. Then think about all the things a tree requires to live well, such as fresh air, clean rain, healthy soil, sunshine, seasons, caring and protection.

Paint or draw all these things around your tree. Then think of all the things the tree provides for others, such as clean air, shade, food, beauty, a home, roots which hold soil from washing away, a branch to hold a swing. Paint or draw these ideas around the tree. Display this mural where everyone can see it.

When visiting your adopted tree friend throughout the seasons, begin your time together by repeating the **"sensing circle"** experience found on page 11, in "To Be A Tree". What do you observe each time? Pay attention to subtle sensations or special feelings that may arise regarding your relationship with your tree. Allow time to express these feelings by drawing pictures, writing some "po-e-tree", or singing a song after each visit.

"My Roots Go Down"

My roots go down, down to the Earth
My roots go down, down to the Earth
My roots go down, down to the Earth
My roots go down.

I am a pine tree on a mountainside
I am a pine tree on a mountainside
I am a pine tree on a mountainside
My roots go down.
My roots go down, down to the Earth......

I am a maple tree giving my sweet sap
I am a maple tree giving my sweet sap
I am a maple tree giving my sweet sap
My roots go down.

My roots go down, down to the Earth.....

I am a child growing on this land
I am a child growing on this land
I am a child growing on this land
My roots go down.

My roots go down, down to the Earth.....

Music by Sarah Pirtle

♠ Make up your own verses to this song!

🍃 **How might it feel to be like a tree**, securely rooted in one place? Do you have any favorite places in Nature that you wouldn't mind being rooted to for a while? Draw a picture of yourself in this special place and tell someone why it is so meaningful to you. Plan a group picnic, or visit this special place.

INDOOR TREE OF MANY SEASONS

Can you imagine a tree growing right inside your home or classroom? An indoor tree can be a tree you have cut from the woods, or a tree you have potted up and brought indoors. It can be a center piece for your tree mural, or the beginning of your indoor winter forest. Set it up indoors near a window, in a nature corner, or near a weather or calendar area. On this tree you can recreate and celebrate seasonal events that reflect the life of your "adopted tree friend".

☙ If you have cut down a tree to bring indoors, support your tree in a Christmas tree stand or in a bucket filled with stones. You can also make a wooden tree stand by nailing 2x4 scraps into the shape of an "X". Anchor the tree base into the center of the X with 18 penny nails or a lug bolt. If you don't want to cut down live trees from the forest, carefully transplant a young tree seedling with all its roots intact. Bring it back to the classroom and treat it as part of a living indoor forest!

🍂 Beneath your indoor tree, create a **seasonal moss garden** to mark the cycles of the seasons. These cycles can be demonstrated by:

- **adding colorful cloth** beneath the moss to reflect the changing seasons
- **decorating the moss** with foraged acorns, stones and crystals, fallen leaves, and fungus
- **changing the fallen leaves** from green to rainbow colors (if you dip the leaves in wax they will not dry out)
- **adding critters** sculpted from beeswax or designed from natural objects, like pine cone animals, or milkweed pod mice
- **dangling snowflakes** from barren branches
- **adding spring buds** and forcing bulbs in pots below the tree
- **making nests** for returning birds

Want To Do More?

🍂 Tell about the changing cycles of your indoor tree or adopted tree by creating a seasonal **"story in the round"** with your friends. Pass a twig around from person to person. The twig symbolizes a "talking stick": only the twig-holder may speak. Everyone takes a turn contributing to the story line. The first person begins the story with a sentence or two, then passes the twig to the person on his left. This individual becomes the new storyteller, adding a few lines and passing the twig when he is finished. When the circle is complete, you will have woven together a story-in-the round.

TREES FOR LIFE BACKPACKS

In a home-made backpack you can carry and care for all of your nature study materials. Make one backpack for the whole class or hiking club, or make your own individual backpacks. Ask some parents or elders to help you out with this exciting project.

Backpacks may contain the following **handy tools** for exploring nature such as:

Magnifying lenses which can be worn
    around the neck
Magnifying boxes for observing seeds,
    crystals, or insects
Journals
Writing or illustrating materials
Broken crayons for rubbings
Blindfolds
Feely bags
Leaf Presses
Home made identification guides to trees
    and leaves
Hats and mittens for cold weather

You will need:

24" x 15" heavy fabric, such as canvas, corduroy, or denim
thread
needles
sewing scissors
velcro, button or snap fastener

(continued)

Directions:

1) Trim a 3 x 24 inch strip from the fabric so that you have a 12 x 24 inch piece leftover. The thinner strip will become a strap, sewn right sides together and turned inside out. The larger piece will become the pocket of the backpack.

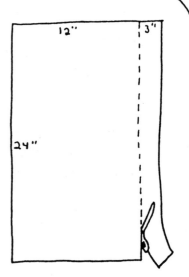

2) Fold the large material like an envelope as shown:

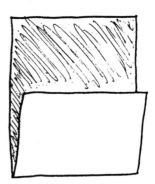

3) Stitch edges, right sides together. Turn inside out.

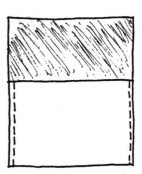

4) Turn the flap edges under a quarter inch, then a quarter inch again. Pin in place. Using a running stitch, secure the edges.

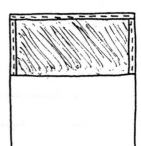

5)   Add velcro, button, or snap closure to the flap:

• Velcro has two parts. Stitch into position.
• After button is stitched in place, determine the position for the button hole. Cut a slit to accommodate the button and make a buttonhole stitch around the buttonhole.
• Apply a snap by sewing the two parts into position.

6)   Fold the strap in half lengthwise. Stitch.
Stitch the strap to the inside of the flap, *or* cut it in half and stitch one half to each side of the back.

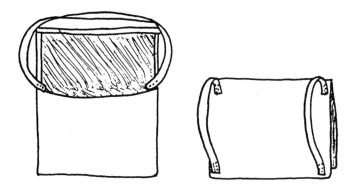

7)   Design a **"Trees For Life" Logo** to decorate your backpack.

AUTUMNAL EQUINOX

The rhythms of the Earth create a natural clock for the plant and animal kingdoms. How do human communities respond to the rhythms of the Earth?

🐾 A special event called the **Autumnal Equinox** occurs each year on September 23. You might say the Autumnal Equinox is like the birthday of Autumn. Equinox is a word that means "equal night", and on this day the Earth is bathed in sunlight the same amount of time as it is bathed in darkness. If you counted the hours of sunlight and hours of darkness, they would be equal. How many hours are in a day? How many hours are in a night on the Autumnal Equinox?

At the Equinox we receive the abundance of the **Great-Give-Away**. It is a time when the community is busy preserving food, gathering with family to express gratitude and celebrate the harvest, and, gradually, preparing for the forthcoming Winter months. What seasonal rhythms and events occur where you live?

♠ Long ago, the people of the Earth found something special about the Equinox and coming of Autumn. What do you observe as Summer ends and the Autumnal Equinox arrives?

♠ Can you describe the changing rhythms on the Earth's landscape where you live?

♠ What new rhythms occur in the human community where you live?

♠ How are families preparing for Winter?

♠ In what ways are members of your community helping each other prepare for Winter?

♠ To find out what is happening to the length of daylight, watch the sunset or the first evening star for the next four weeks.

Does the sun set before or after dinner? Does the sun set before or after going to bed?

♠ Create a celebration on the Autumnal Equinox. Invite your family and community. Build a bonfire, decorate pumpkin lanterns or candles to illuminate this festive event, tell stories, share harvest foods and song, stack the woodpile for an elderly neighbor - do something to bring warmth to your community.

"The Gift of Fire", which takes place during the season of the Autumnal Equinox, is a dramatic telling of a story about the bringing of fire - and its light and warmth - to humans long ago. It's a wonderful story to act out - and to retell to your family and friends. Turn the page and listen to what Grandforest Tree has to say....

"The Gift of Fire"

I am old, but not so old as my great-grandfather. He can remember all the way back to the days when the people of the Earth had no fire to keep them warm during the cold winter months. Listen to the story he told me of the Gift of Fire.

"Once there was a tribe of people known as the Fire Keepers. They lived isolated from all other humans on a windy mountain surrounded by a dense forest. The Fire Keepers were stingy and kept the fire to themselves. Suspicious of strangers, they turned all visitors away, living in constant fear that someone would take some of their precious fire.

"Each fall, as the wheel of the year turned farther and farther away from the sun, the days grew shorter and colder. The weakening sun did not have the strength to fully warm the earth before retiring again to its bed in the west. This is when the people without fire suffered most. Having long since given up attempts to get fire from the Fire Keepers, they accepted their fate and huddled together through the long nights, trying to keep warm.

"One morning a young boy was out gathering water. Despite the brilliant sun, the day was bone-chilling cold and windy. As the child was scooping water from a river, he heard coughing and sputtering coming from upstream. Glancing over, he saw a frightened rabbit trying to scramble up a log that was lodged against some rocks. The rabbit soon tired and let go, floating downstream towards the little boy. Knowing - yet not knowing - that this was no ordinary rabbit, the child pulled the rabbit from the freezing water and gathered it in his arms. He placed the miserable creature beneath his robe. Grabbing his bucket of water, he raced back to his home, a little house of ice and snow.

"Once inside, he placed the rabbit in sleeping skins. Soon the animal's wet fur began to dry and the rabbit stopped shivering. The child fed it some stems he had gathered from

beneath the snow. The next day, the grateful rabbit hopped about as if nothing had happened, and seemed anxious to go back outside. Before it left, however, it surprised the family members who gathered for their mid-day meal by suddenly speaking to them.

"'People of the ice-house, thank you for taking me in and nursing me back to health.' It nuzzled the little boy, giving him a special thanks for saving it from the cold torrents of the stream. 'As you know, I am Rabbit, the trickster, imbued with special powers. In gratitude for saving me, I shall make an attempt to get fire from the Fire Keepers so you will no longer need to suffer through the cold and darkness.' With that, Rabbit hopped out into the snowy winter cold, making his way to the lonely, windy mountain of the Fire Keepers.

"When he reached the entrance to the Fire Keepers' village, Rabbit disguised himself as a puppy that had porcupine quills in its muzzle. Dogs were the Fire Keepers' one weakness - they loved dogs, especially cute fuzzy puppies. Dogs were their best friends and helped them guard the sacred fire.

"Rabbit's plan worked. The guard at the gate took pity on him, and pulled out the quills. Rabbit-pup wagged his tail and licked the face of his new friend. The guard did not have a dog, and decided this was as good a time as any to adopt one. Soon Rabbit-pup was living in a warm tepee. He was even given a name - Quill, after the quills in his muzzle.

"Now, it was the custom of the Fire Keepers to honor all the guardians of their village, whether they be human or dog. When Quill grew a little older, they held a ceremony to welcome him into the Fire Keeper Family. As part of the ceremony, Quill had to wear a feathered headdress and stand as close to the fire as he possibly dared. Unknown to anyone, Quill secretly made his own feathered headdress and coated it with resin. Moments before the ceremony, when no one was looking, he switched the headdress they had given him for the one he had made.

"Rabbit, alias Quill, sat proudly while the villagers began to dance around the fire. Sitting close to the fire, he kept bowing his head as if in approval of the fantastic dances the people performed. Suddenly, just as the dancing reached a feverish pitch, Quill bowed his head into the fire, lighting his headdress! With lightning speed, Quill ran between the startled villagers' legs and out into the night. He raced down the mountain, the dogs and villagers following close behind him.

"Rabbit ran and ran until he was exhausted. When he could go no further, he called for crow to help him. Crow swooped down from the sky and scooped up the fiery headdress in its claws. Rabbit - who was now a rabbit again - disappeared down a rabbit hole. The Fire Keepers' dogs stopped at the hole and pawed furiously, whimpering and barking in excitement. In their frenzy, they did not notice Crow, wheeling away with the fire. (To this day, some of the dogs are still searching for Rabbit. If you ever see dogs chasing something in the tall grass, or excitedly sniffing a hole in the ground, you can be sure they are probably relatives of the Fire Keepers' dogs!)

"Crow flew high in the sky, cawing a warning to the other animals that the Fire Keepers were angry and wanted their fire back. All of the animals pitched in to help. Some of them distracted the pursuing dogs and Fire Keepers by running every which way. Other animals ran a relay, taking turns carrying the fire when one or another grew tired. Eventually they delivered the fire to the people of the ice-house, who shared it with all the peoples of the Earth.

"Ever since that time, people have honored the gradual return of light and warmth. This honoring not only celebrates the Earth's turning toward the Sun, but it also recalls Rabbit's heroic feat of bringing fire to the people. And since all the animals helped carry the fire, humans should remember to respect them - even the smallest ones!"

EQUINOX STAINED GLASS WINDOWS AND LANTERNS

You will need:

Windows
colorful, freshly fallen leaves
waxed paper
crayons
old candle
grater
newspaper
iron
glue
construction paper

Lanterns
poster board
scotch tape
masking tape
votive candle
small jar to hold candle

To make a stained glass leaf window:

1) Gather up beautiful, freshly fallen leaves.

2) Place the leaves on a piece of waxed paper.

3) For extra color, add crayon or old candle shavings to the waxed paper. (Crayon or candle wax shavings may be made by rubbing old candles or old crayons on a potato grater.)

4) Place the sandwiched leaves and wax paper between a layer of old newspapers.

5) Iron the leaf and crayon sandwich until the waxed paper and shavings seal together.

6) To create the stained glass leaf window, cut 2 frames from construction paper. Glue or tape the frames onto each side of the waxed paper. Hang these "stained glass leaf windows" so that the light passes through them.

To make a Stained Glass Leaf Lantern:

1) Iron two or four waxed paper leaf windows of the same size.

2) To make the lantern form, cut a piece of poster board five times as wide as the waxed paper and four inches longer than its height. Now fold the poster board into four even sections. Each of these sections will house a leaf window.

3) Cut out a window or frame shape in two or four of the sides. The number of window or frame openings you cut should match the number of waxed paper leaf windows you have made.

4) Using scotch tape, mount the waxed paper into the inside of each window. Tape the poster board inside the end seam so that the lantern can stand up solidly. This may require a strong tape, such as masking tape.

5) Place a votive candle in a baby food jar that has some water in the bottom. Light the candle and place the lantern over it. Sit around your lantern and sing some of your favorite Autumn songs with your family or friends.

TREE FOR LIFE: A JOURNEY WITH APPLE TREE

Autumn is the season to celebrate the fruits of the harvest! Now is the time to begin a seasonal, year-long journey with the apple tree. Close your eyes and take a trip to the apple orchard to see what's going on in the life of the apple farmer and the apple tree.

Mmmm, crunch!" There's nothing as crisp as a juicy apple that you pick yourself on an autumn day. Have you ever stopped to think about what it takes to get a ripe juicy apple to your mouth? Look around the orchard at the full branches laden with apples. Smell the sweet, apple aroma that wafts through the autumn breezes. Look at the shape of the old, gnarled yet sturdy branches that curve and bend and hold the fruit. Each apple tree looks as if it is bending to the Earth, to offer its apples to passers-by. What does the stature of the apple tree remind you of? Do you see one tree which looks like a gentle old woman tossing crumbs to the pigeons in the park?

Next time you polish your apple on your shirt sleeve, take a careful look at the shiny apple. You might discover some of its hidden secrets. At the end of the delicious, ruby-ripe fruit of the apple is the stem. This is where the apple once held on to the parent tree. What else do you see? At  the bottom of the apple is the remainder of five, dried-up triangular shapes. That's all that's left from the apple blossom. If you look into the cavity that surrounds the former blossom, you might find hair-like bristles deep inside. That is all that remains of the pistil and stamen, once found in the center of the fragrant apple blossom.

There are still other mysteries to solve, but in order to

discover any more secrets you must cut the apple in half, horizontally. Inside the apple you may see a surprise more beautiful than you ever imagined. A wonderful, starry chamber is found within the apple fruit. This star within the apple still holds the

shape of the blossom which began its life. Do you remember the cloud of apple blossoms that perfumed the orchard in May? If not, let's go on a journey through all the stages you missed before this juicy apple came along.

Imagine yourself in the orchard during Winter when the apple tree is sleeping. Often people believe that nothing important is going on in the life of a wintering apple tree. Well, it may be a time for rest, but it's also a time of preparation and protection. This is the time of year when the apple farmer prunes the tree, thinning its branches and removing old growth.

The apple tree is gathering the special, secret magic which helps the apple grow. You see, the secret of the apple star is protected, tucked away inside the winter bud. Within the bud, five pointed green sepals will form to surround the five petals of the May apple blossom. The winter chill and dark starry nights work some of the magic that helps the bud to awaken in Spring. Without the quiet chill of Winter, the bud would never feel the call of Spring.

Spring is long awaited in the apple orchard. Early in the season, the apple farmer goes to the orchard to look for the "silver tips", which are the first changes to appear on the tree. Bud scales are like a winter coat that protect the tiny bud all Winter. When the bud scales are pushed away, the silver tips hidden beneath are revealed to the apple farmer.

What color do you think the farmer sees next? Green tips, which burst out of the silver bud case. These are the leaves, wrapped up in a tight bunch. There is something hidden inside these leaves. The bud of the apple flower is wrapped inside! Five green sepals make the shape of a five-pointed star - just like the one that was dried out on the base of the apple! The farmer is happy to see the sepals, which resemble the shape of the star.

Next, the farmer spies the blossom bud peeking out from inside the green sepals' covering. But before the blossom fully opens, it will perform a magnificent color dance for the farmer. Each blossom will begin as red, change to pink, and then to white, draping the orchard with perfume and clouds of soft color! Five shimmering petals dance above the green star sepals, which cup the blossom to the sky.

Apple blossoms are grouped in clusters of five. The very first blossom to open to Spring's beckoning is the "King Blossom". King Blossom sits in the center of the other four blossoms, which will soon follow with their own colorful bloom-dance. It is more than just the farmer who notices the King

Blossom, though! Hungry bees come to gather nectar and pollen. With it, they will make more honey to feed the bee colony, whose winter honey supply may be all but gone. Dancing bees dust the golden pollen of Spring on one blossom after another. The orchard sings with the sound of thousands of buzzing bees visiting the apple blossoms.

The King Blossom will be the first to lose its petals, as it was the first to show them. Then the remaining apple blossoms will drop their petals, too. Next time the apple farmer looks at the apple trees, they will no longer look silver, or red, or pink, or white. What color will they be?

Now the apple trees look green, and the farmer notices the beginning of baby apples among the leaves. The tiny apple is the shape of a fuzzy green ball, firmly holding the five star sepals in place as a reminder of Spring's arrival. But now the starry sepal no longer looks skyward. It dangles down toward the Earth, along with other fuzzy, green balls clustered close by.

In June, the apple farmer will be grateful for the "June drop", when many of the green balls fall from the cluster. Only one or two baby apples will remain to grow from the cluster into ripe apples. You see, it would not be possible for the apple tree to bear all these green balls to a ripe fruit stage. The apple leaves cannot make enough food to feed each and every one of these fuzzy young apples. It takes the energy of forty apple leaves to transform each blossom into a ripe, juicy red apple! Soon the green balls will lose their fuzzy coats and begin to resemble the smooth fruits of Autumn.

All Summer the apple farmer cares for the orchard as the apples grow. The roots of the apple tree spread as far as the tree branches reach, way beyond the trunk of the tree. The hidden roots are carrying water and nutrients to feed the growing tree and its growing apples. A new fruit bud, home for next year's bud and apple, grows along the branch tips. The star sepals at the blossom end of the apple dry out as the apples slowly ripen. By Summer's end the apples are green and full, unless hail, drought, insect or disease weakens them.

As Autumn arrives, the orchard is transformed into a ruby-red and soft-green glow. Both the orchard and apple farmer feel full. The harvest is ready to begin! Anticipation and wonder fill the air, for the apple's secrets still lie hidden deep within the starry chamber. The apple farmer is excited to hear a new song buzzing in the orchard - apple pickers and families, come to enjoy the gifts of the apple tree! And the secret of the star inside the apple waits to be discovered, to share its story and plant anew its seeds of wonder.

&❧ **Celebrate the apple tree** with any of the following activities:

   ♠ **Draw the "seasons of color"** that the apple farmer sees in the apple orchard. Begin with the colors of Autumn, and work your way through the seasons to Summer.

- ♠ **Draw the events** in the life of an apple farmer, demonstrating each of the four seasons.

- ♠ How many ways can you **eat, cook and enjoy apples?** Try making apple sauce, apple muffins, apple cider, apple salads, apple jelly!

- ♠ Can you **write your own story** about apples and how they might change your way of looking at the world?

- ♠ **Apple art projects** using apple drops are fun. Try making apple head puppets and star apple prints.

- ♠ Continue to **study your apple tree "for life"**. Make seasonal visits, observe its changing ways, and become its caretaker.

Want To Do More?

🍎 Become an **apple farmer apprentice!** Visit a real apple farmer to find out more about the year-round tasks necessary to keep an apple orchard healthy, such as pruning, planting new apple trees, insuring the pollination of apple blossoms, and organic methods of protection from insects and disease. Join the farmer as he picks apples, presses apple cider, stores apples for Winter or sells apples. Invite him to make apple head dolls with you. Ask him lots of questions!

🍎 Illustrate the development of the **five-pointed star.** Begin with the arrival of the first Spring sunbeam. Follow it as the star becomes hidden inside the apple and is finally discovered by a hungry human!

🍂 There are many **stories about apple trees**. Read the story of Johnny "Appleseed" Chapman, and the story about the apple that fell on Isaac Newton's head and helped him understand gravity.

TREE FOR LIFE: A JOURNEY WITH MAPLE

Can you believe that you have to wait until Autumn to see the Maple leaf reveal its true colors? That's right, hidden beneath a hand-shaped leaf of green, lies a brilliant golden yellow, orange or red leaf waiting to do its rainbow dance in the Autumn skies! Grandforest Tree is wise in the ways of Maple Trees, for he is one himself. Listen as Grandforest Tree tells his story:

L isten to the autumn winds carrying messages across the landscape. What are the winds telling you? We Maple Trees know the restless breezes are a signal that the days are growing shorter. Soon, our lush green leaves that waved like flags during Summer will no longer change sunlight into food for us. We will store all our nourishment inside, sending food to every root so we can survive the upcoming Winter. Green leaves will no longer cover us, and our true colors, hidden beneath the green, will begin to show. We will drop our leaves to the Earth in a brilliant rainbow carpet. Then we prepare for Old Man Winter to come. I am very old, and have shed many coats of glorious leaves as I waited for the arrival of my frozen friend. I am very old, and I am very wise."

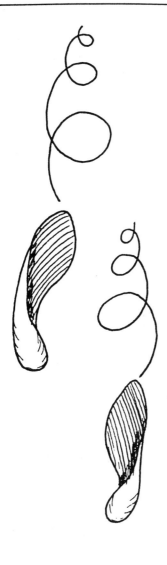

≈ If you adopt a Maple tree for the year, watch to see which rainbow colors it will reveal to the harvest skies. You might also notice that the autumn winds carry the flying **helicopter-like seeds** of the Maple tree far from the parent tree. Why is that? It's fun to toss the seed helicopters to the wind and watch them in action!

≈ You may notice that seeds carried far from the parent tree land on the lawn or bare Earth of the thick forest floor. What will happen to the seeds as they spend the Winter months hidden beneath the frozen snows? The hard, dry seed coat will protect the soft seed within the papery wings. Pull apart a Maple seed to discover the parts that make up this interesting seed.

Grandforest Tree continues:

"When you look at us in Winter, you probably think there is very little activity going on. If you look closely, though, you may see more. Our naked silhouettes stand against the winter sky, revealing strength and beauty gained from years of growth. If you could see what is wrapped inside our bud cases, you would know that we are getting ready for Spring to come. After a full winter chill and a period of quiet, we will be ready to receive the message of Mother Earth, calling us once more to life.

(continued)

"Our Spring Songs may be heard in the sugar bush near Winter's end, as the "ping-ping-ping" of our sap hits the buckets. When the days begin to warm but the nights are still freezing, our sap can be collected, for we are beginning to draw life-giving sugars from our roots up to our buds. Yes, indeed. Our sweet syrup signals Winter's end! The Maple farmer is busy this time of year, hanging buckets and hauling the watery sap that we stored inside our trunks all Winter. When enough of our sap-water is collected, the Maple farmer boils it to make thick maple syrup. I am so old I have sung many Spring Songs. The Maple Farmer has collected enough of my sap water to make syrup for 2,000 pancakes!

"The Maple sugaring season ends when we awake and our buds swell. For now our sap carries food from our roots to our young leaves, which are snuggled inside their bud cases. After our buds burst open to reveal leaves, we will begin to make our own food again. We will transport this food to every twig and root to keep all our tree parts growing. That is why I am so big, the tallest tree in the forest! I am very old, and I am very wise."

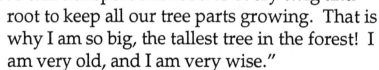 Around the Spring Equinox (March 20) and thereafter, look at the bud cases of older Maple trees. You may notice downy, **sunshine-colored bud cases** along the branch ends. Remember when the tree withdrew its energy inside itself at the end of Autumn? Hidden beneath the bud cases is the

nourishment the tree stored away during Winter for this Spring's growth. Look for the Elder Maple tree's shimmering display of sunshine-colored buds.

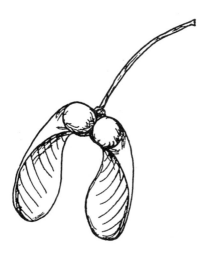

🐚 Sometime later you may notice the **dangling clusters of yellow Maple tree flowers** changing the tree's color from gray to golden. Spring breezes will carry pollen to the swaying flower clusters. Soon after flowering is completed, **yellow baby leaves** will emerge in four or five pairs. Looking closely, you may notice that the hand-shaped leaves are arranged in a pattern of opposites. As Spring evolves, the yellow baby leaves will grow and become a **bright green**, producing food for the tree's growth.

🐚 As you cast off your winter jacket in Spring's warm sunshine, Maple seeds will cast away their protective winter coat. These **helicopter seeds** wintered under a blanket of snow, and are ready to settle down and grow. If the **tender seed** can take hold in the Earth, a root will fasten it securely to the land and it will wander no longer.

🐚 Soon after the root secures the tiny Maple seed, you may notice two long, skinny, limp leaves shaped like bananas. Does this scrawny little **seedling** look ready to withstand the world of the forest? Next, the young seedling will send out more sturdy leaves, but not the familiar hand-shaped leaf of the Maple tree we all love. Two tiny triangular leaves appear above the limp banana-shaped leaves. Keep on watching, for soon the young Maple will reveal its

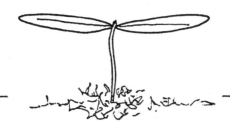

true hand-shaped leaves, which will burst forth from the tip of the stem. They will appear in a cluster of four or five pairs of leaves, announcing to the forest, "I am here!"

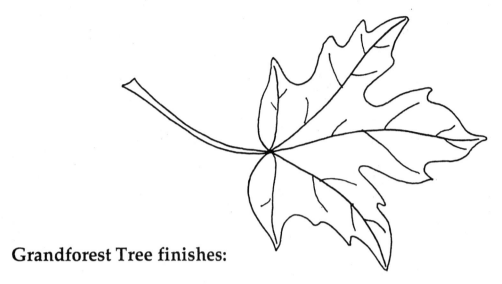

Grandforest Tree finishes:

"When I was only two years old, most of the spring woodland wildflowers towered over my head. By the time I was five years old, I was almost to your shoulder. When I was ten, I was almost twelve feet tall! How tall were you when you were two? When you were five? Who grows faster, you or me?

"Throughout the Summer, I will be hard at work making new buds at the tip of my twigs. Although I am very old, my leaves use the sun's energy to make and store food for all my growing parts. New bark is growing inside of me. If you look at a younger tree, you can see where the old, outer bark is cracking and stretching to create some growing room. What happens to your outer coverings as you grow bigger? Hidden beneath the Earth, my roots spread as far as my branches reach out. My helicopter seeds grow larger and larger all Summer, until the autumn winds carry them away.

"Some of us live for as long as 300 or 400 years. As we grow, we dance the rhythm of the seasons. Cloaked in snow, our gray, naked forms hold the promise of Spring in our buds, which burst open after our sap begins to flow. All Summer we hide beneath our green leaves. And when the cool breezes return, we reveal our rainbow colors of Autumn.

"I have danced through many seasons, and sung the songs of many years. I, Grandforest Tree, am very old. And I am very wise."

Honoring the Maple Tree

ᥱ⚘ Show the Maple tree in every season: make a watercolor painting in Autumn, sketch the silhouette of your favorite Maple tree in Winter, create a tissue paper collage of the Maple in Spring, make leaf rubbings of your tree's canopy during Summer.

ᥱ⚘ During sugaring season, visit a Maple farmer working in his spring sugar bush. Boil some Maple sap to see how the Maple farmer makes syrup.

ᥱ⚘ Look for a young emerging Maple seedling in the Spring. Where is the closest parent Maple tree? During the seasons of the year, observe and record in drawings the life story of a young emerging Maple tree and a parent tree.

ᥱ⚘ Act out some of the secret activities of a tree. We can't see these things happening because they occur inside the tree.

TREE FOR LIFE: A JOURNEY WITH WHITE PINE

Perhaps not until late Autumn, after the trees have dropped their rainbow colors, do you notice the ancient White Pine Tree, quiet as a feather upon the landscape. Now may be the perfect time to take a closer look at these silent sentinels.

Grandforest Tree Speaks:

I want you to meet my friend, Ancient Pine.

"Long ago, in early Summer, Ancient Pine held up its new shoots, candle-like pine twigs covered with golden stars. The twigs were also decorated with pinkish flowers that were the beginning of pine cones. After the pollen settled on the flowers, the pine cone-to-be closed up and cradled the growing seeds inside. When the pine cone was ready, about two years later, these pine seeds became food for squirrels or seed for future generations of Pine trees."

"The hungry squirrel prepares for Winter's arrival,

collecting pine cones and cones from other evergreen trees that drop these tasty morsels to the Earth. Squirrel knows that only the Pine tree can make pine cones. How many cones from evergreen trees have you found and called "pine cones"? The other evergreen trees each make their own cones, all named after themselves, such as "fir cones" or "hemlock cones".

🐿 Would you like to learn more secrets about Pine trees? Find a pine cone. The best place to look for one is beneath the parent tree. Look at it carefully, for inside every pine cone lies the secret to Ancient Pine tree's ability to survive since the days of the dinosaurs. A cone that is all closed up probably won't reveal its secrets to you right away. You'll have to take it home and put it in a warm oven. This will help to dry the cone so that its scales open outward. When the scales have spread open, place the pine cone in a paper bag and shake it well. Can you find the tiny seeds that have fallen out? If you could look beneath the scale of the pine cone, you would find two winged seeds cradled there. These are the seeds that the squirrels search for deep inside the pine cone.

🐿 Did you find your pine cone right underneath the parent tree? Does this look like a good place to start a family of young pine trees?

🐿 Fortunately for the Pine tree - and the squirrel - each parent tree produces many pine cones. As the squirrels come and collect pine cones, they often carry the cones far from the parent tree, and as the squirrel eats the pine cones some of the seeds scatter in a suitable place to grow. The little pine seeds you found inside the pine cone got their start just about this time two years ago.

Grandforest Tree Continues:

"Ancient Pine tree has no reason to be concerned about the arrival of enduring cold, winter temperatures. Often Pine trees look like white, winter tipis scattered across the landscape, wrapped over a green cloak of pine needles. No matter how fierce the winter weather, Ancient Pine seems to hold up under cold and heavy snow all Winter long."

🐚 Look closely to see how it holds its branches. Are they pointed up or down? How does the shape of Pine's branches help it endure a heavy snowfall?

🐚 Crawl beneath the sheltering lower branches just like rabbit or fox. Look up, and you may notice that Pine's five branches whorl around its central trunk. Some say that Pine grows one whorl every year of its life. Can you estimate how old the Pine tree you have crawled under may be?

🐚 Looking up again at the five branches that radiate like spokes of a wheel, can you imagine a way to connect the end points of the five branches, like dot-to-dot, and draw a five pointed star? Notice the bark of Ancient Pine. See how the bark stretched as the tree grew taller and wider over the years, outgrowing its smooth skin of earlier days. You may even discover the fragrant but sticky pine sap on its trunk. This pine sap helps to heal the wounds of Pine tree over its lifetime.

Grandforest Tree Finishes His Story:

"Ancient Pine's feather-like clusters of five needles are more delicate than you may have imagined. Most of the time you see fresh green needles, but close inspection may reveal brittle brown clusters of needles, hanging like clothespins on a clothes line. These needles are shed over the years, little by little. You often hear the green, feather-like needles sighing when a wind passes through Ancient Pine. If you are lucky, the wind may sing through the branches of Ancient Pine when you take shelter beneath it. Listen to the songs and enjoy the protective, peaceful feeling Ancient Pine gives you. In the Winter hush, you might receive one final gift - stories of days long past. For Pine trees are known to live for two to three hundred years.

(continued)

🍃 Illustrate your discoveries of White Pine's secrets. Try watercolor "resist paintings" with craypas. First, draw your Pine tree with craypas. Add a watercolor wash for the sky and other details. The craypas will "resist" the watercolors, adding a nice effect to your artwork.

🍃 Tell a story that White Pine told you.

LEAF MAGIC

A leaf performs several jobs, and hides many mysteries within its thin green skin. Did you know, for example, that trees actually make their own food? That's right: no cook books, no practice necessary. It's something trees do from the moment of birth. How? The following experiments may help you find out.

You will need:

♠ **Experiment 1:** Are leaves like kitchens?

Maple tree leaves

♠ **Experiment 2:** Have you ever wondered why a plant needs water?

celery
2 plastic cups
food coloring

♠ **Experiment 3:** Do leaves get suntans too?

water
scrap paper
paper clips

♠ **Experiment 4:** Do leaves perspire?

terrarium
plant to put into the terrarium

♠ Experiment 1: Are leaves like kitchens?

🐛 Look at a leaf up close to observe what can be seen with the ordinary eye. What do you see? Now hold a leaf in front of a sunny window. Can you see more? Stem, veins, edges, green areas should all be visible. Leaves are actually **food factories** for trees and plants. They process ingredients from the sun, water and air, as well as minerals from the soil, into food for the plant. Can the food factory be seen with the ordinary eye?

♠ Experiment 2: Have you ever wondered why plants need water and where all the water goes after you water the plant?

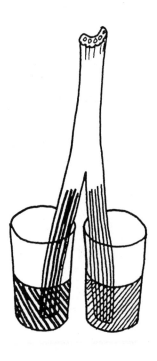

🐛 Try this. Cut a stalk of celery halfway up the stem. Place the two halves, cut side down, into two glasses of water. Add a different color of food coloring to each glass. Now place an uncut stalk of celery in a glass that contains no water. Put the glasses containing the stalks of celery in a safe, cool place and observe them in the morning. What happened? Can you explain why?

If you look carefully at the celery stalk, you may see **veins,** or channels, which move water and nutrients through a plant. Can you find the veins in a celery leaf? If the food coloring did not rise into the leaf, hold it up to a bright light and you will see its tiny waterways.

♠ **Experiment 3: Do leaves get suntans, too?**

🍃 Cover part of a house plant's leaf (or perform the experiment on a tree). A scrap of paper secured with a paper clip works well. Leave the cover on and keep the plant in the sun for a week. When you remove the paper, what do you see? Is the area that was deprived of sunshine a different color?

The covered part of the plant may be yellow, because without adequate sunshine it has been unable to create the green life force, or food, for the plant. The life-giving substance is created when sun, air, water and nutrients mix together to create a sugary, liquid food.

This life-giving substance is called **chlorophyll.** It travels throughout the entire tree and plant, nourishing all its parts. The scientific term for this process of food-making is known as **photosynthesis**. The invisible green cells of plants perform this magical process.

Did you notice **leaves in the Spring** that were **yellow** when they emerged from their bud cases? After the leaves starting making their own food they turned green, the color of chlorophyll. But their yellow color remained hidden beneath the green chlorophyll. And so in Autumn, when the tree begins preparations for its journey into Winter, it no longer makes food, and the yellow color reappears. Do you remember seeing young budding leaves in the Spring that were red? Now they've also shed their green chlorophyll mask, revealing their brilliant selves to all the earth and sky!

😊 **Record and illustrate** what you observe during visits to your adopted tree. Pay attention to two or three particular leaves. You might begin an account in your journal entitled "Diary of An Autumn Tree". Every few days, or at least once weekly, return to visit the leaves. In your diary, illustrate any changes you observe in color, size, freshness or shape. If your friends have chosen their own trees, compare the different autumn changes in the trees.

♠ **Experiment 4: Do leaves perspire?**

😊 Place a plant in a terrarium. Observe the terrarium for a week or so. Do you see moisture condensing inside the terrarium? The invisible parts on the leaves, called **stomata**, are like lips or mouth parts, which release the extra water the plant does not need. The moisture released by the plant forms drops on the terrarium walls. If you sit beneath the shade of a tree on a hot summer day, you can feel the cool moist air that the tree creates. This moist air, which may feel like air conditioning to you, is a refreshing gift from the trees.

LEAF PRESSES

A handy, pocket-size leaf press is just the right size to carry on the trail. You can make it using recycled materials.

You will need:

Corrugated cardboard, cut into two 4"x6" pieces
Newsprint or manila paper, cut into five 8"x6" pieces
Rubber bands
Markers, paints, crayon or nature magazine photos, and a little glue

To make the press:

1) Cut two pieces of corrugated cardboard approximately 4 x 6 inches.

2) Decorate the outsides of the cardboard with paint, marker,   crayon, magazine, recycled wrapping paper, collages, or whatever you like.

3) Put your name inside.

4) Cut five pieces of paper 8 x 6 inches and fold in half to measure 4 x 6 inches.

5) Place manila papers inside the cardboard covers and wrap the completed press with rubber bands.

6) To press leaves, choose small leaves that will fit in the press. Place leaves carefully inside manila folders, then wrap the press securely with rubber bands, which will put pressure on the press.

7) Allow a couple of weeks to press and dry leaves. If you can't wait that long, you may press the leaves between paper with an iron on the "permanent press" setting.

There are many ways to use pressed leaves!

🍂 Save pressed leaves for **tree identification guides** or future **tree art projects.** Enjoy pressing leaves over and over again!

🍂 **Laminate** pressed leaves with clear contact paper and hang in windows for a festive autumn display.

🍂 You can **store samples of laminated pressed leaves** from each tree species you study. Keep them in the EARS shelter or near trees in your yard or school yard. An oversized yogurt container with a lid can safely store many index card samples for future reference.

🍂 **Identify pressed leaves** using a tree book recommended in the bibliography.

MATH, NATURE'S WAY: SPIRALS AND CYCLES

There are many hidden patterns, numbers, shapes and movements in Nature. The Pine Tree is fun to work with when exploring the secretive world of nature shapes. Here are just a few ideas to get you started.

&❧ How can you reveal the star hidden within a pine whorl? Make a **Pine Star Weaving**. Gather some fallen limbs from the Pine forest and look for a section that still has five whorling branches. By weaving yarn around these branches, you will reveal the hidden star.

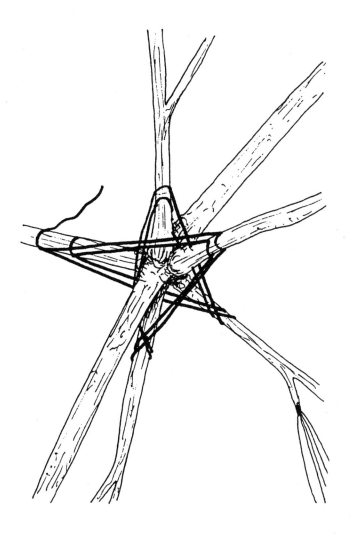

You will need:
(fallen) pine branches
with 5 whorls
colorful yarn

1)   Using the colorful yarn, start at the top center of the whorl, as though it were the top point of a star, draw the yarn down to the bottom left arm of the star. Weave the yarn around the whorl.

2)   Now draw the yarn diagonally upward and wrap it around the upper right arm of the star.

3)   Then draw the yarn across and wrap it around the opposite arm of the star.

4)   Next draw the yarn down and wrap it around the

lower right arm of the star.

5) Finally, draw the yarn back up to your starting point, at the top center point of the star.

6) Continue this weaving pattern until a star emerges that is at least two inches deep. And there it is, the hidden star in the Pine tree revealed!

✍ Did you know that **pine cones hide a nature pattern**, too?

You will need:

pine cones and
yarn or
clay or
paint

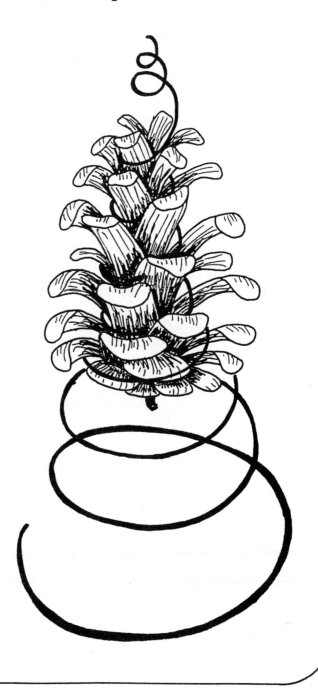

Look closely at the pine cone to see if you can find its secret pattern. It is easier to see the pattern if you lay a piece of yarn along the pine cone, beginning at the top and following the scales down. You should see a spiraling pattern as the yarn follows the path of the pine scales. You may also press the pine cone into clay or dough to make an impression of its patterns. Or, paint alternate scales or rows of scales on the pine cone to reveal the hidden patterns.

✍ **Spirals and cycles**
exist everywhere in nature. In a cycle and spiral, everything

returns to a state close to the starting point, but not exactly the same. The following activities may help demonstrate some of the cycles and spirals found in the natural world.

You will need:

lots of friends
salt or sand
crayons
scissors
paper
dominoes
yarn
sticks
clay

♠ Create a **Friendship Spiral Dance**. Dancers stand in a circle, hands on the shoulders of the person in front of them. The leader breaks the circle shape and gradually spirals inward to the center. Eventually she turns outward and begins traveling back along the path she journeyed in on. Try to move with this form while singing a song or round, such as "I Have Promises to Keep" or "Happiness Runs In a Circular Motion".

♠ The **Lap Game** is played as children stand in a circle, shoulders touching. Everyone then turns sideways, facing in the same direction. Maintaining a tight circle, each stares at the back of the head of the person standing in front of her. On a given signal, the leader slowly squats and sits on the lap of the child behind him. The second child will immediately begin to sit on the lap of the child behind her - and so on. When all are sitting supporting each other, raise hands outward and cheer!

♠ **Form Drawing** makes it easy to feel the motion of spirals. Using a broken side of a crayon for shading, illustrate a circle and a spiral on large paper. Notice how this pattern or motion reveals itself to you over the next week.

♠ **Spiral Mobiles** can be designed from paper circles. Begin cutting

on the outer edge of the paper and spiral inward until you reach the center of the circle. Suspend mobiles from their center point and watch the wind play with them.

♠   **Block Domino Spirals** may be built and knocked down. Use blocks or domino table blocks.

♠ **God's Eyes** are woven from sticks and yarn. The pattern will appear rather square when finished, but the weaving is done in a spiraling motion. Cross two sticks to form an "X". Start at the center and weave the yarn round and round.

♠ **Clay pots** may be designed by coiling plasticene, beeswax, dough or clay into snakes or snail shapes.

♠ **Sing rounds** and observe the spiral of sound.

♠ **Vortex explorations** are exciting. Observe the spiraling motion of water as it runs down a sink drain. Or, create a funneling tornado in soda bottles. To observe this phenomenon, fill a soda bottle with water. Add glitter to the water to give it a sparkling effect. While holding the bottle upright, turn another empty soda bottle upside down on top of it so that the two openings meet. Holding the openings together, invert the bottles so that the water from the filled soda bottle swooshes like a tornado into the empty soda bottle.

♠ **Pendulum art** imitates the Earth's spinning motion by dripping sand or salt in a spiral pattern from a suspended cone or funnel.

♠ **Somersaults and cartwheels** are spiraling motions that are made using the body. Every Autumn, maple "helicopter seeds" spiral through the air to the Earth, creating a motion that is not much different from a somersault or a cartwheel.

PO-E-TREE

"I think that I shall never see
a poem as lovely as a tree."

The magnificence of trees has inspired many poets. This famous quote is from Alfred Joyce Kilmer, a young man who grew up in New Jersey during the turn of the century. Do trees inspire you to write poetry? Here are some examples of simple rhythms you can use to write wonderful verses.

Nature Verse: a descendent of Haiku

In traditional times, Haiku poetry's subject was nature. Today, however, it might be about any subject. Still, the reader should have the sensation of hearing, smelling, tasting or touching something. While Haiku always has a fixed three line form of which the first and third lines have five syllables, and the second line has seven syllables, Nature Verse can have any amount of syllables as long as the first and last lines are always shorter than the middle line. Here are some examples:

light
up under the gull's wing
sunrise

✦ ✦ ✦

bass
picking bugs
off the moon

✦ ✦ ✦

old pond
frog leaps in
water's sound

Cinquain

A Cinquain consists of five lines, with two, four, six, eight and two syllables, respectively. Some examples follow:

> These be
> Three silent things:
> The falling snow. . the hour
> before dawn. . owl on the wing
> at dusk.

❖ ❖ ❖

> Sea foam
> and coral! Oh,
> I'll climb the great pasture
> Rocks and dream mermaids in the sun's
> Gold flood.

GIFTS FROM THE TREES: MAKING FOREST DYE

For many hundreds of years, people have used the gifts of the trees to add color to their lives. Autumn is the time to harvest these tree gifts to make your own dye baths. But don't expect brilliant, crayola-type colors from Mother Nature's forest children. Most of the colors are soft and muted.

Color some wool or cotton scraps for Autumn weaving projects and experience the beautiful colors of nature!

You will need:

> black walnut hulls or butternut hulls
> sumac fruit
> bark from birch, elm, maple, hemlock or alder trees
> lichen
> goldenrod
> onion skins
> marigold flowers
> large pot for boiling
> undyed cotton or wool fabric or natural yarn
> alum
> washing soap

ꙮ Native people use **Black Walnut hulls** for a light brown color. You will need a pound of hulls for each pound of fiber you wish to dye. Soak the hulls overnight. Then boil them for twenty minutes. After boiling, strain away the hulls, leaving a dark dye bath. Add four gallons of water to the dye bath and let it cool.

In the meantime, **mordant** (fix the color so it won't run or fade) the cloth or fibers to make the dye hold fast. To mordant one pound of cotton or wool fibers, make a mordant bath. Add four ounces of alum (alum is a powder easily obtained from a drug store), and one ounce of a sodium carbonate soap (such as Ivory Snow) to four gallons of water. If you are dyeing cotton, moisten the cotton and stir it into the mordant bath until the

water reaches the boiling point. If you are dyeing wool, place it in the mordant bath but *do not stir* it unless you want to make felt! Boil the fibers for one hour, then let them sit overnight in the bath. When you are ready to dye the fibers, remove them from the mordant bath and squeeze. The fibers are now ready to be placed in the dye bath, and will retain their new color for a long time.

After placing the fibers in the dye bath, heat at a low boil for one hour. Cool the fibers in the dye bath. Then rinse free of residual colors, and air dry. You will find your fibers colored a beautiful light-brown, reflecting the natural colors of Mother Nature!

๛ **Seasoned (dried, one-year old) Butternut hulls** offer a rich black hue.

๛ **Sumac fruits** share their orange-red color.

๛ Colonists used **forest trees** for brown and gray dye, and took advantage of the natural **tannin** content in these trees to mordant the fibers. Use one pound of bark from yellow or sweet birch, elm, maple, hemlock, or alder tree. Soak the bark overnight in two to three gallons of water. The next day boil it for one hour. Or, for a darker dye, boil it for several days. To remove the bark, strain through cheesecloth or a colander, then add your cloth to the dye bath. Let it soak for one hour, then hang it up to dry.

๛ **Lichen** provided a range of quiet colors to the Native Americans who used them. Can you guess which colors? Experiment and find out! Lichens can be used for dyeing without having to mordant fibers. Remember to use one pound of dye materials for each pound of fiber you plan to dye.

๛ **Goldenrod, marigold flowers or onion skins** are bright, golden tones, which contrast nicely with the darker forest colors made from tree dyes. Mordant fibers with alum beforehand. Soak dye materials in water and boil until the plants lose their color. Strain off plant materials and add four gallons of water. Cool. Add pre-mordanted fibers and bring to a boil. Simmer one hour. Cool, rinse and air dry.

๛ Small individual **lap looms**, or one large loom, can be constructed using four equal size, sturdy branches. Tie the four branches so that they

form a square frame. Warp cotton string vertically onto the loom. To create an Autumn tree weaving, weave dyed yarn, cotton strips, pot holder loops, even unspun wisps of fleece, horizontally into your loom. For a special effect, add tiny fir cones or tree seeds to your weaving.

　　🐾 Or make a **round loom** using grape vine. Round looms tend to wobble less than square ones. These make nice door ornaments.

AUTUMN LEAF ART:
LEAF BANNERS, LEAF MOBILES, BRANCH WEAVINGS, T-SHIRTS, CARDS AND STATIONERY

There are endless ways to enjoy leaves in art projects! Just add a little imagination to the gifts that trees already offer!

❧ Leaf banners

You will need:

  leaves
  leaf press
  paint (for outdoor banners, use permanent fabric paint)
  brush or roller
  wood or cloth for banners (for outdoor banners, use fabric)

1) Gather and press leaves.

2) Paint one side of the pressed leaves with a brush or roller. (Waxy leaves may not work well, so it is wise to experiment before printing on the banner.)

3) While paint is still wet, place leaves on wood or cloth.

4) Press carefully with roller or fingertips to make a leaf-print

5) Or, for banners or signposts around your EARS station, draw oversized leaves.

Beautiful banners will surely make people stop and notice special trees along the EARS trail!

❧ Lotto Memory Games

You will need:

pairs of pressed leaves
Poster board or 4x6 inch cards
clear contact paper
crayons
scissors
ruler
pencil

To make the memory cards:

1) Measure and divide two pieces of poster board into 4 x6 inch sections.

2) Laminate the leaves to the 4 x 6 cards with contact paper. Since the object of the game is to find matching pairs, make sure each leaf has an exact match on another card.

3) Color the backs of the cards with crayon, paints or markers.

To play Leaf Memory Lotto:

1) Shuffle the leaf lotto cards, then place cards face down on the floor.

2) Each player may turn over two cards at a time, looking for a matching pair of leaves.

3) If the player gets a match, the pair may be removed from the lotto board.

4) If no match is found, both cards are turned face down and returned to their original place.

5) The next player turns two cards over looking for a matching pair. The game continues until all matches are discovered.

♠ Advanced players can try to name the tree leaf of the matching pair before removing the cards from the playing area.

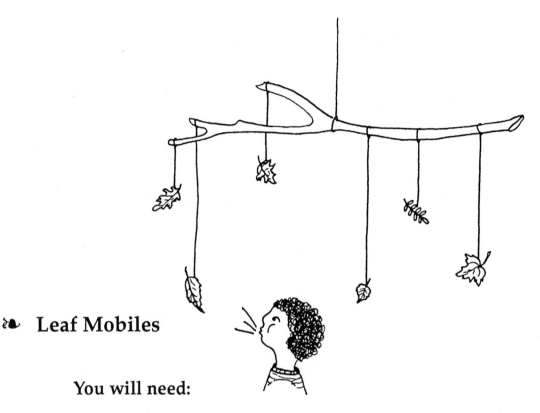

🍃 Leaf Mobiles

You will need:

        pressed leaves
        clear contact paper
        white thread or yarn
        interesting sticks or driftwood

1) Laminate pressed leaves between two pieces of clear contact paper.

2) Cut out the laminated leaves, leaving a 1/4 inch border of excess contact paper for a seal.

3) Use white thread or yarn to suspend the leaves from interesting sticks or driftwood. Watch how they sway in the breeze, imitating the motion they made when they grew on the tree.

🌿 Branch Weavings

You will need:

> forked branches
> multicolored yarns
> leaves
> feathers
> pine cones

1) Find branches that have a fork or crotch in them.

2) Weave multicolored yarns around the forked ends to create a "warp", or weaving area.

3) Fill in this area with more yarn and add extra touches like leaves, feathers and pine cones.

4) For an interesting or unusual decoration, plant branch weavings in the lawn or garden areas around your home or school.

5) Or hang the weavings from the wall or ceiling by adding a string handle to the weaving.

🌿 Trees for Life T-shirts

You will need:

> fabric paints
> pressed leaves
> t-shirts

1) Apply a <u>thin</u> layer of fabric paint on pressed leaves, then press the leaves onto t-shirts.

(continued)

2) Or make leaf rubbings on paper with fabric crayons, then iron the rubbings onto t-shirts.

A great way to make a fund raiser to earn money for local tree projects!

🐦 Trees for Life Cards and Stationery

You will need:

> crayons
> paper and envelopes

1) Simply make leaf rubbings on paper, or laminate dried leaves to cards, writing paper or envelopes.

These make great gifts, or they can also be sold at a fund raiser.

I Am A Tree Halloween Costume

Can you create a tree costume for Halloween? Make a Halloween Leaf Camouflage Mask. Or dress up as a part of a tree, and sing a song to explain who you are.

❧ Halloween Leaf Camouflage Masks

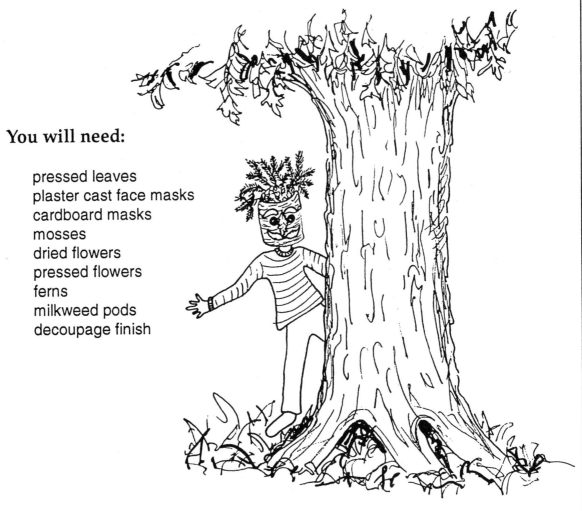

You will need:

pressed leaves
plaster cast face masks
cardboard masks
mosses
dried flowers
pressed flowers
ferns
milkweed pods
decoupage finish

1) Apply dried pressed leaves to plaster cast face masks or cardboard face masks. Be creative with mosses, dried flowers, pressed flowers, ferns, and milkweed pods.

2) Make eyebrows, beards, moustaches and laminate natural objects to the mask with decoupage finish. This will help preserve color and texture.

♠ Play hide and seek in the forest on a Halloween Eve Trail. Pretend to be a "spirit of the forest", hiding while others try to find you. Give a trick or treat to each person who discovers you!

❧ Halloween Tree Parts

You will need:

pressed, waxed leaves
paper
brown paper bags
drinking straws

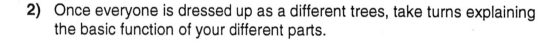

1) Wear your Halloween camouflage mask, or make a crown of pressed waxed leaves. Make paper branches, attaching leaves to arms and hands. How about wrapping your body with brown paper for the trunk?
Demonstrate what is happening beneath the trunk by making a paper vest covered with drinking straws. Let one straw stick out and attach a sign that says "sweet sap here!". How would you show roots coming out of your toes?

2) Once everyone is dressed up as a different trees, take turns explaining the basic function of your different parts.

❧ Share a "Tree Rap" performance Halloween Night!

Josie's "Tree Rap" Song

"I am a tree
I wear a crown on my trunk.
You can't see my roots
Cause they're usually sunk
Deep in the Earth
Where they like to sink
While they're holding me up
And bringing me drink.
Deep inside, you might like to know
Are the magical parts
All are helping me grow.
First layer's the bark
Protecting me from disease.
The inner bark carries
Food down from the leaves.
Cambium's doin' whatever she please
Inner bark, sap wood, making tree rings.

If you counted the tree rings here
Then you would know
How long this tree
Has been trying to grow.
Sap wood is carrying the juice to the leaves
Then letting some go up into a breeze.
Leaves cleaning the air
Which has been dirtied by man
Where can you find
Others working so grand?
Fruits and nuts
Give all food to live,
I ask you, how much more
Can anything give?
Heartwood is holding the whole thing together
From the beginning
Through all kinds of weather.
Standing up tall
The heartwood's delight
Is seeing that everything
Reaches the light.
Don't waste a minute
Now that you know
How this awesome tree
May be helping you grow.
Find a way to show you care
For trees that give beauty,
Food and clean air!
Next time you see a tree
Don't give a shrug
Spread your arms wide
And give the tree a hug.
Yes, spread your arms wide
And give the tree a hug."

J.D.

TREE COOKIES

Can you look at a living tree and guess its age?

🐾 How can you tell if the tree was born before or after you? Does the breadth of a tree determine its age? Hug a tree. Do your fingers meet at the other side? Will this tell you how old a tree might be? What about the height of a tree? Will it tell you a tree's age? Set up your own guidelines for determining a tree's age, then try some tree cookies to test your theories!

Tree cookies are not something to eat, though they are a lot of fun to make! Tree cookies are an exciting tool for determining the age of trees. You might want to place a tree cookie near your EARS Station and use it to demonstrate how to tell a tree's age.

Make a **Tree Cookie** to find out how old a tree or tree-stump is!

You will need:

    bow saw
    tree stumps or limbs

♠ There are several ways to make a tree cookie. Find a tree that has already fallen in the forest. Simply make a fresh cut with a bow saw across the trunk to reveal the tree rings. Make another cut a few inches above the other, and now you have a tree cookie!

♠ If there are no old tree stumps around, slice a one- to two-inch thick piece of tree cookie from a firm tree limb in your wood pile or from a fallen tree. When making the cut, try to cut through the limb smoothly so you won't disturb the visibility of the tree rings. Make a tree cookie from a tree species similar to your adopted tree, or from any tree located near the EARS Station.

♠ If you know that each circular ring of the tree represents a year of growth, you can **estimate the age of the tree cookie.** The

light-colored areas show the Spring's growth, the dark rings represent the Summer's growth. So to discover the tree's age, count only the dark *or* the light rings.

♠ Sometimes it is necessary to count tree rings several times as some tree rings are very close to others. What might cause tree rings to be very close together? Closely spaced rings mean that very little growth took place that year, perhaps due to drought or trees growing too close together or other unusual circumstances. Larger spaces between rings show heavier growth. What size was the tree when it was your age? What is the tree's general **history of growth?**

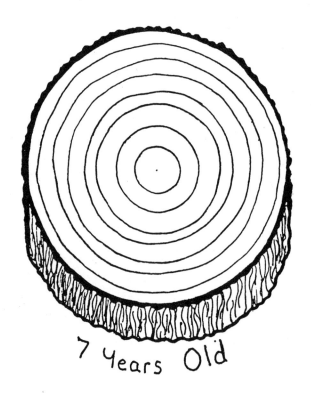

7 Years Old

♠ Here is another way to determine a tree's age, though it is quite challenging. **Try counting the leaf bud scars** below each leaf growing on a tree's twig. Or, estimate a tree's age, like some people do, by counting whorls of branches on evergreens, one year for each whorl. (Add four years for the development of the first whorl.)

♠ One final way to count the age of a tree is to plant one yourself and **count each birthday you celebrate together.** Or find a tree that you think is about your age and celebrate birthdays together year after year.

Want To Do More?

🐦 A tree cookie can demonstrate historical events that occurred during the years the tree lived and grew. Since each ring represents a year, you can match special happenings with particular rings. Push pins with little paper flags attached can be placed in the tree cookie to mark **significant historical events.** Create illustrations to show the stories hidden within trees, such as the year the tree was born, the year the school was built, birth years for the children and teacher in the class, birth dates for family members, or other significant historical events in your community.

⚜ **Draw a tree cookie representing the life of the tree in the following story.** Demonstrate how the tree rings grew wider or thinner according to the events in the life of the tree.

Once upon a time, a young tree grew beneath its parents in a forest nursery. It was glad for the shade of friendly trees, for the the sun was hot that first summer. It seldom rained, and young tree didn't grow much beyond the skinny wisp it was when first born.

"The next few summers, the rain clouds often visited. As the young tree drank the water, it felt its roots dig deeper into the Earth. The fifth year, a young rabbit nibbled off most of its branches. Without leaves to make any food, it barely grew an inch. The next two years passed quickly and the little tree grew vigorously.

"One day, however, a young child celebrated her seventh birthday in the forest. The next day she returned to the forest, dug up the tree and planted it near her home. That year the tree grew little, as all its energy was spent healing its severely severed roots. During the years that followed, the girl visited the tree often, and each Fall she gathered the colorful leaves that the tree dropped. Each Winter, she dreamed of the day the tree would grow limbs strong enough to hold her tree house . . . ."

♠ **Make up a story** that describes all that the tree saw during its lifetime. You might wish to consult Grandforest Tree for ideas.

WALKING WITH GRANDFOREST TREE

What have the ancient ones, Grandfather and Grandmother Trees, seen over time? What stories could these Wise Elders tell? What changes have they witnessed?

&⬧ This guided journey takes you on a trip back through time. The reading is best shared outside beneath a large, old tree in the forest or in a meadow-thicket. If you are lucky enough to have access to both a meadow-thicket and a forest, walk from the meadow-thicket into the forest during the reading. You can also enjoy this guided journey indoors. **Just relax and listen to the words of Grandforest Tree as he spins a tale of days gone by.**

I am very old and very wise. I have seen many things in the fields and forests that surround me. I know all that has happened here. Listen while I tell you of long ago days.

"A long, long time ago, when I was just a sapling, the land was mostly forest. However, farmers were settling the land, and they began to clear the forests to make fields. They cut down trees, and gathered rocks and stones to make fences. Soon much of the forest land was broken up into fields for grazing animals, for growing hay and cultivating food. In my part of the forest, hardly a tree was left standing. The land on my south side was cleared for a meadow - the clearing came right up to my roots!

"I was lucky enough to escape the axe - the farmer decided I would make a good shade tree. And what a wonderful shade tree I was, standing on the edge of the forest overlooking a beautiful, sunny meadow! I quickly grew from a sapling to a full grown tree. I grew so tall, in fact, that not even the deer could nibble on my tender winter buds. My ever spreading branches created an inviting pool of shade, my trunk was thick and strong, and my

roots thrust deeply into the soil.

"I was very happy and never lonely. In Spring the farmer would tickle me with his drill, making holes in my trunk, then place buckets beneath the holes to collect my sweet sap. Can you guess what he would do with the sap?

"Summer after summer, cows and sheep rested in the cool shade of my leafy arms. Children climbed into my branches and built a tiny tree house. Later they tied an old tire to my thick middle branch. Spring through Fall, children's laughter filled the air as they excitedly whooshed back and forth, singing and laughing. Sometimes they swung high enough to touch my leaves! These children hugged me all summer long!

"But one day, the laughter came no more. The cows and sheep disappeared, and the tire hung forgotten, swinging only to the song of breezes. The family had moved south, where the winters were shorter and the growing season longer. Oh, how I missed the children and the animals who once sought the shade and comfort of my branches. All I could do was to wait and watch the seasons change, and to hope a new family would someday make its home nearby. It was a very lonely time.

"I wasn't lonely for long, though. A pair of warblers nested in a crevice between two branches, happily gobbling up the ants and insects that also lived in me. Soon some gray squirrels set up home in my upper branches. These furry creatures never seemed to tire of running up and down my trunk, gathering sticks for their cozy nest, or scampering about in search of nuts and seeds.

"Squirrel stored several caches of food nearby, so that on the coldest winter days he would not have to go far to find food. Of course, Squirrel forgot where some of these caches were, and after several winters his seeds began to sprout. Before long, a couple of tiny oak trees and several baby pine trees surrounded me in the meadow. And, of course, many of my own children began to sprout up, pushing their tender new maple leaves up towards the sunshine. Each year, the wildflowers grew more and more abundant.

"Over time, the open meadow began to change as hardy

plants that loved the sunshine began to grow there. Aspen, Staghorn Sumac, and White Pine, as well as thorny berry bushes, began to sprout up along the edge of the field. The bushy Juniper, with its sharp needles and dusty, white-blue berries, slowly spread over the ground, forming a thick, prickly mat. Hawthorn, another little tree with sharp thorns, sprouted in various parts of the field. The field became a meadow-thicket.

(Walk to the meadow-thicket if there is one nearby)

"The plants were wonderful hiding places for many animals and provided food for them. Deer, rabbits and grouse joined the squirrels, mice and birds. Foxes found the hunting excellent, although they avoided the prickly juniper!

"Many, many mysteries surround you in the meadow-thicket. Notice how the quality of light changes in the meadow-thicket. Listen to the birds chirping and flocking to find food, to the wind as it flows across the field, to crows cawing in the distance. Feel the touch of the wind on your cheek. Touch the sharp needles of the juniper, or the soft twigs and fruit of the Staghorn Sumac. Take a deep breath through your nose. What do you smell? Break open a frosty-blue juniper berry, and take a whiff. What does the bark of the white pine smell like?

"It wasn't long after the shrubs moved into the meadow that a colony of my fellow maple saplings made their way into the field from the north. Oh, how wonderful it was to have some of my own kind to talk to! I often told them stories of days gone by, just as I am telling you now. They grew big and strong, shading out the sun-loving plants - the Juniper, the Aspens, White Pines and Spruces. The meadow-thicket was becoming a forest once again! Woodland flowers began to spring up everywhere. Beech, Butternut, and Ash trees joined the Birches and the Maples. Needle-leaved trees sprouted whenever a sunny window opened up, creating the healthy, mixed forest you see today.

(Walk into the Forest)

"The forest has many surprises and secrets to discover. Close your eyes and breathe in the aroma of the forest. What do you smell? The earthy fragrance of lush vegetation or decaying leaves? The spicy essence of needle-leaved trees? Listen to the wind - what do you hear?
Are the leaves rustling in the trees? Is the wind singing through the pines? What other sounds do you hear? Open your eyes. What do you notice about the play of light and shadow? Hug a nearby tree, pressing your cheek against its trunk. Feel its rough texture. Look closely at the bark. What does it remind you of? What animals do you think live here?

"Yes, the meadow-thicket and the forest seem like very different places. But they are closely related. Long, long before forests existed, when Earth was very young, there were only fields of rock and stone. These rocky meadows eventually grew grasses and shrubs, and finally forests formed. So remember - if you cut down the trees, you have a meadow, and if you leave the meadow alone, it grows back to a forest. The place where you are standing might once have been a forest.

"Many creatures are dependent on both the meadow and the forest. The deer seek the shelter of the trees, especially in Winter, but in the warmer months they venture out into the open spaces. Grasses, Staghorn Sumac berries, and fallen apples are among their favorite foods. The owl sleeps in the forest by day, but favors the fields for hunting at night. Many forest birds enjoy the seeds and sunshine of the meadow-thicket. Fox roams through both woods and fields, looking for tender tasty mice and rabbits to eat.

"So, you cannot separate the meadow-thicket from the forest or any other habitat. Although there are many different kinds of places on earth, everything is interdependent and intertwined in the wonderful dance of life.

"And that is just a snapshot of what I have seen, and what I know. I am very old and wise. Almost 200 years have passed since the trees that surrounded me as a sapling - my parents, grandparents, sister and brother maples - were cut down to create a field. Eventually the field was abandoned. It became a meadow-thicket, then grew into a forest once more. And now my children and grandchildren grow beside me."

♠ You might want to **illustrate the story of succession** on a mural or series of overlays. Draw the first small plants becoming a meadow. Next, draw the emerging meadow-thicket. Finally, draw the emerging forest.

FOREST TERRARIUMS - BRINGING NATURE INDOORS

Bring nature indoors and watch it grow and change with the seasons by creating mini-habitats of the forest for desktop observation or for a nature table display.

You will need:

> terrarium - large bottles, or glass containers such as goldfish bowls
>   or small aquariums
> sand
> charcoal
> potting soil
> bottle cap or seashell
> small rocks
> pine cones
> small pieces of bark

To make a terrarium:

1) Place a one-inch layer of gravel or coarse sand in the bottom of your container for drainage. Then add a thin layer of charcoal chips to absorb odor. On top of this layer, add enough potting soil to support the plants and mosses.

2) Recess a small seashell or bottle cap into the base materials of the terrarium to represent a miniature pond. Re-fill the mini-pond with water as it empties.

3) While hiking one day, forage for terrarium specimens such as mosses, tiny pine cones from hemlocks, lichen on a rock or piece of bark, or young small ferns. Be sure to collect specimens by gathering the roots and soil ball intact. Do you know how to identify protected or poisonous species? A call to your local Forest Service can answer this question.

♠ **Observe and record changes** in the terrariums over the seasons.

Terrariums make lovely gifts for a senoir citizen or shut-in on any holiday - or any day at all!

🐦 You might enjoy reading <u>Small Cloud</u> by Ariane, which tells about the journey of a drop of moisture, like the ones you may see forming inside your terrarium.

THE BIRTH OF A FOREST

Did you ever wonder what a forest might look like if a tree never grew there? Take a hike with friends to discover what makes a forest a forest. This is a good time for each friend to be responsible for a different task that will help the group make discoveries about the forest. A cooperative learning group makes it easy to solve mysteries.

🐛 While you are visiting the forest with your friends, try this. A few steps before entering the forest, **form a long caterpillar**, with everyone holding onto one another's waists from behind. Everyone should close her eyes and carefully, slowly step into the forest, right foot first, then left. Be aware of feelings or sensations around you. Continue along for a minute or two in silence, listening to the forest hush, the musical notes of birds, feeling the absence of sunlight, smelling a rich full forest, sensing the gentle protection of the forest canopy as it shelters you, feeling the cushion of forest floor under foot. Walk along until everyone has had a chance to experience the forest in this quiet way.

How did the Forest come to be?

You may work in several small **cooperative learning groups** or one large one. The cooperative learning task might be to discover answers to the following questions:

- What are the ingredients of a forest?
- What are the *four most important* ingredients of a forest?
- What are the *two least necessary* ingredients of a forest?
- Can you list the ingredients of a forest in order of their age?

You may **organize your group** by dividing up the tasks among the members. When working in small cooperative learning groups, it is important to emphasize that the success of the group depends on the contributions of each individual. Since the entire group is responsible for the successful outcome of the activity, each group member should feel supported by the whole group. To begin, the group should identify a recorder, spokesperson, supply caretaker, group leader, trouble shooter or any other role that seems necessary.

♥ The **group leader** can help organize the group and insure that the tasks flow smoothly. She can also keep track of the passage of time and keep the group focused.

♥ The **recorder** is responsible for making a list of all forest ingredients identified by the group. How many ways can members of the group support the recorder in this task? Each person could offer spelling suggestions to the recorder, if necessary.

♥ The **group spokesperson** is a communicator for the group. The group spokesperson must listen to all the conversations among the group and, later, relay the main thoughts of the group to the entire class.

♥ The **supply caretaker** is responsible for the care of any equipment used during the activity.

♥ A **trouble shooter** assists the group in accomplishing its tasks, especially when questions or challenges arise. She also resolves conflicts among individuals and, when the group wanders from its purpose, helps the group get back on task.

♠ At a given signal, such as an owl hoot, the group leader should call all the cooperative learning groups together to **form a large circle to share some of the information discovered**. By discussing all the ingredients that make up a forest, you will begin to understand how a forest becomes a forest!

MEET YOUR FOREST COMMUNITY

Are you ready for a tour to meet your forest community? As with a human community, each member of the forest community holds an important position and performs a special job for the benefit of all the community members.

🐌 On your next forest hike, look for the **nurse trees** of the forest. Can you guess what nurse trees might do in a forest? Nurse trees shelter a new generation of evergreen trees with their canopy or roof. They provide just enough light and plenty of shade for the nursery bed where evergreens grow. What species are the nurse trees? Aspens, birches? The nurse trees also provide care for the evergreen young. In the Autumn when nurse trees drop their golden, shivering leaves like rain, they mulch and feed the growing young trees.

🐌 After many years of this good care, the evergreens will rise above the nurse mothers and eventually shade them, depriving the nurse mothers of necessary sunlight. Eventually, a rich, lush forest of evergreens will replace the nurse trees. Then the nurse trees will find a resting place upon the Earth as their soft, old wood falls to the forest floor. Here they shall give away the last of their life force, creating more soil and making way for yet another generation of young trees.

🐦 Can you find any **plants growing below the tree canopy** or tree roof? Shade-loving ferns, shrubs and herbs grow among the wildflowers. Where do shrubs like to live? Are they located beneath the sky holes of the forest roof? Shrubs grow quickly and must take advantage of the light before the sky holes close over.

🐦 Do you see any **grasses** in the forest? Why or why not? What kinds of plants make up the ground cover in a forest? What is the role of these wildflowers, ferns and herbs?

🐦 Can you find the **clean-up crew** that inhabits the forest floor? Some may be too small to see with the eye. Others are hidden from view beneath the leaf litter. Others may have left signs of their scavenging along the forest floor. Peek beneath the leaves and see if you can find the little critters who make up the clean-up crew.

🐦 Before you leave the deep part of the forest, stop to look at the leaves of some trees. What shade of green are they? Pick one or two of these leaves, noticing the type and size of the host tree.

🐦 Now find a tree in the sun that is the same size and type as the shaded tree where you picked the leaf specimen. Pick a leaf or two and compare them. Are the leaves the same size? The same color?

Often, trees that get plenty of sun have smaller leaves than those that grow in the shade. This is because they do not have to "stretch" to collect sun rays, as do their relatives in the darker parts of the forest. The leaves

may also be a lighter shade of green than the tree leaves of the dark forest. This is because there are fewer, cholorphyl-producing magic green cells in the smaller leaf.

🍂 What are some terms for the different plant communities that dwell beneath different light patterns of the forest. Which plants represent a **canopy** or roof? Do you remember the **understory** of growth created by the younger trees? Did you see a shrub layer? Where was the herb layer found? Which inhabitants create a **foundation** on the forest floor?

🍂 As plants join together in a community to create a forest, they create something which is a great **success.** When one habitat changes into another habitat it is called a **succession** of growth. Can you act out the forest succession? Begin with a single tree and re-create what happens as a seedling takes root and springs to life. Show the stages of its life as it becomes a nurse tree, then a mature tree. Now show the different roles, or jobs, other types of plants perform within the forest community. Members of this community might include baby trees, shrubs, herbs, wildflowers, stones, mosses, leaf litter - and all the other large and tiny inhabitants who reside in the forest.

🍂 Can you act out the forest succession scene as a **web of life?**

FOOD WORKS IN THE FOREST - A WOODLAND PICNIC!

Let's have a picnic in the woods and discover how food works in the forest. But first, think about all the hungry plants and animals that the forest has to feed in the Fall. You will discover that you're not the only one who likes a picnic in the woods!

Materials for the hike may include:

paper bag or basket, or backpack
several small flags or markers
food scraps such as:
    peanuts
    orange peels
    apple cores
sunflower seeds
corn from your garden
a picnic for yourself

🐦 It might be helpful to **designate a specific area** or clearly defined boundaries for the hike and the food works experiment. Decide whether or not you want to return with samples of "eaten objects" for a display.

🐦 Buddy up with a hiking partner and search for one example of something that's been eaten - or look for a critter eating something. When you find a sign of food working in the forest, hold up your hands clasped together and call out **"Food Works in the Forest!"** Other buddy groups will come running to see what's been found. Try to figure out what might have consumed the food you found.

🐦 **Look for clues** to identify who's been eating what - such as tracks, tooth marks, holes in leaves, chewed nut shells, feathers or bones, mushrooms, berries, even scat.

♠ You may discover holes in mushrooms made by a hungry **slug**. Look for a glossy trail around the mushroom to confirm the identity of the picnicker.

♠ Maple leaves lying on the forest floor often have round holes in them. A **small worm** chewed these holes, the same way a can opener opens a can. If you search carefully, you might find small circular cuttings lying on the earth. Look inside the round leaf sandwich. Most likely you'll see a small, worm-like larva there!

♠ **Staghorn Sumac** trees found on the edges of the forest may have broken branches where the fuzzy red fruit clusters were once attached. Deer love to browse on these during their Autumn picnics.

♠ Don't forget to look in the leaf litter layer of the forest floor! Search for **tiny insects** breaking down the leaves into rich soil. Mmmmm. Delicious!

♠ Check beneath loosened tree bark for burrowing insects and larvae. **Engraver beetles** leave a "treasure map" design behind to show that the inner bark is one of their favorite dining spots.

🍃 At the end of your hike, place food at different locations in the forest. Mark each site with a flag. What do you think will happen to the food? **Record your predictions**, explaining what you expect to happen.

🍃 Did you find that you were so hungry that you ate your woodland picnic, too?

🍃 If there are any mysteries remaining to be solved about how food works in the forest, write these questions, along with some illustrations, in your nature journal.

🍃 Make a return hike to the food sites to see what happened to your food offerings. Were your predictions proved true or false?

TREES FOR LIFE SCAVENGER HUNT

This is an exciting way to test your knowledge of tree leaves. To prepare for the scavenger hunt, make a "Trees for Life" Scrapbook. Each page heading should describe a particular leaf or object you will be hunting for. When the leaf or object is found, it can be preserved by mounting it on the correct page in your scrapbook. Then it will become a souvenir of your scavenger hunt!

❧ A **"Trees for Life" Scrapbook** can be made by stapling together blank paper. Each page should be labeled with a heading or illustration of the scavenged object. The goal of the scavenger hunt is to fill all the pages of the "Trees for Life" Scrapbook with the forest objects described.

Here's a list of possibilities:

oval leaf
big toothed Leaf
tiny toothed leaf
hand-shaped leaf
skeleton leaf
cluster needles
scaly needles
skinny leaf
feather-shaped leaf
eaten leaf
young leaf
old leaf
favorite leaf
mysterious leaf
opposite leaves
alternate leaves
unusually colored leaf
winged seeds
tree pollen

Ready, set, go!

You might enjoy sharing scrapbooks with a friend after the scavenger hunt. This will show you the many different possibilities that exist in each category.

A FAMILY UNDER ONE SKY: WEBS OF LIFE

We are all one family under one sky, and we all are dependent upon one another. Create a web of life to show how life works in the forest.

"The Family of Life"

The weaver of life
wove a web,
each strand a different being.
The web buzzes, hums, barks, talks, growls,
howls, sings sweet spring songs and is silent.
It swims, runs, hops, wriggles and walks, and soars in the sky.
Rooted in the earth, it sways in the wind.
Life and death, predator and prey, seeds and soil, plants and animals -
each and every living thing -
holds several silver strands,
linking life with life.
This web of life
holds all life,
embraces life.
This web of life
is the family of life:
One family
under one sky.

J.H.

⁐ Webs of Life are a wonderful experience for helping you to visualize the inter-connectedness of nature. Over one hundred years ago, **Chief Seattle spoke these wise words** about the web of life:

"Every shining pine needle, every mist in the dark woods, every humming insect is precious in the memory and experience of my people. The sap that runs through the trees carries the memories of my people.

"We never forget this beautiful Earth, for it is our Mother. We are part of the Earth, and it is part of us. The perfumed flowers are our sisters; the bear, the deer, the great eagle are our brothers. The Earth does not belong to us, we belong to the Earth. Whatever befalls the Earth befalls the sons and daughters of the Earth. This we know. All things are connected."

Adapted from Chief Seattle's Address, 1854

🕊 Recite these wise words of **Chief Seattle** whenever you make a web of life. Though his words were spoken in **1854**, they are just as important today as they were then.

🕊 **To make a forest web of life**, each person represents a forest member she is fond of. Design and wear a name tag illustrating your identity. Are you a tree? A fern? A toad? A bug? Each forest member may describe what is pictured on her tag.

♠ Form a circle to start the food web. A forest member representing the Sun stands in the center of the circle, holding her arms outstretched. A member who depends upon the Sun for life, such as Lichen, holds onto one of Sun's outstretched arms. Soil might take hold of Sun's other outstretched arm. Now Acorn can grab hold of Soil's arm. Oak Tree can grab hold of Acorn's arm. Leaf can grab hold of Oak's arm, Squirrel can grab hold of Acorn's arm - and so it goes and grows, until the last forest member attaches her free hand back to the Sun! What do you think this web means?

🕊 Can you **draw a web of life mandala** in your nature journal? Begin by drawing a circle in the center of the page. This represents the sun. At the end of each sunray radiating out from the sun, illustrate a living thing that depends on the sun to survive, such as an acorn. Above the acorn, draw the oak tree that grew from it. If a squirrel was part of your web, then draw the squirrel sitting in the branches of the oak tree eating an acorn.
(continued)

♠ Is soil part of your web of life? If so, draw soil at the end of another sunray. What does soil give life to? Draw a wildflower growing from the forest soil. Is there a bee on the flower gathering nectar?

♠ At the end of other sunrays, illustrate other aspects of the forest that you discovered on your hike.

♠ When all the sunrays are illustrated, you may find that there are relationships between the objects you drew along the sunrays. These relationships can be joined by drawing a large circle around the sun, which demonstrates their interactions. Soon the sun will be surrounded by a big web showing how the sun's power reaches all around the earth.

We are all one family under one sky, each dependent upon one another.

Winter

OLD MAN WINTREE

Dress warmly for a Winter tree walk and guided journey to meet an amazing character named "Old Man Wintree". This Winter nature walk will allow you to really "get inside" the wintry tree or forest. You can perceive the world as Old Man Wintree might by using your imagination, your senses of touch and hearing, and by paying attention to your feelings. The questions that arise from this experience might be useful in planning further inquiries or investigative activities. Bring nature journals and colored pencils to draw or write with.

> ☛ *Note:* If you don't already have a favorite or adopted tree, pick out a tree that seems to speak to you as you are hiking through the forest.

GUIDED JOURNEY

Before meeting Old Man Wintree, close your eyes. Stretch out your hands as a friend leads you slowly toward him. Keeping your eyes closed, **learn everything** you can about Old Man Wintree. Hug him (to see how fat he is), rub your cheek against his bark (to feel his textured covering), measure his height by reaching an arm up, feel for signs of branches. . . insects. . . holes. . . fungus. . . moss. . . leaf or needle shapes. . . or any other distinguishing features. Listen for sounds of animal life nearby, or the wind dancing through the trees. . . . Put your nose close to the trunk and smell the bark. . . notice how you feel when you are close to Old Man Wintree. With your eyes still closed, tell your friend what you've learned about this tree.

When you are finished exploring Old Man Wintree, walk a few steps away from him before opening your eyes. Find a comfortable spot where you and your friend can see the tree, then

comfortable spot where you and your friend can see the tree, then sit quietly and work in your journals. **You can illustrate** any discoveries you made about Old Man Wintree, or write down any questions you have for him . For example, you might want to ask him the following questions: "How did you get planted here?" "How old are you?" "Why are you covered with moss?" "What kind of tree are you?" "How do you live under snow and ice?"

Want To Do More?

🐚 You can return to Old Man Wintree anytime to chat with him. It might be fun to visit him in late Winter, after you have been exploring trees for awhile. If you go with a friend, take turns standing behind him and pretend to be his "voice". Try to answer some of the questions that have been raised during your explorations. You could begin by saying, "Hi, I'm Old Man Wintree, what would you like to know about me? "

🐚 If you can't return to Old Man Wintree at Winter's end, you might enjoy making a Winter tree mask from birch bark. Wear your Old Man Wintree mask when you speak for him, telling a story about his life.

Winter Tree Mask

You will need:

birch bark, or colored paper that looks like birch bark
scissors
cardboard
staples or needle and thread
objects from nature
glue
string

1) Find a piece of birch bark that is approximately the same size as your face. Only take bark that has fallen from a tree. If the bark is not pliable, soak it in water for a half hour and it will soften.

2) Handle the bark gently as you cut it into the shape desired for your mask.

3) Cut a piece of cardboard that matches the shape of your bark mask. Glue or stitch the cardboard to the mask to reinforce the delicate bark.

4) Sew or staple a cardboard or bark headband to the back of your mask. Measure your head size so the mask will fit properly.

5) To locate your eye area, hold the mask to your face and have a friend draw two small circles with a pencil. Remove the mask and carefully cut two <u>small</u> holes without tearing the bark. It might be difficult to see through the holes, but you want them to be small so that the mask maintains the characteristics of a tree rather than a person.

6) Now for the decorative details. Use your imagination! Decorative objects from nature can usually be fastened to your mask with a stapler. However, in places where there is a sharp curve, like the nose area, you may find that string, glue and a little patience goes a long way.

(continued)

7) Evergreen needles, small tree fungus or tiny pine cones make great eyebrows.

8) A moustache made from two empty milkweed pods might look very distinguished!

9) Your Old Man Wintree mask can even have a headdress - add pine boughs, dried beech or oak leaves to the top of it.

♠ *To prolong the life of your mask, mount it on the wall when you are not using it.*

WOODLAND NATURE CALENDAR

Record the dates of forest happenings - such as snowfalls, bird and animal sightings, bud development, the first blossoms, first flowers, insects, and so on - on a calendar you can make! Keep it for your own use, or give it to someone as a gift.

You will need:

>   grids with 1 1/2 inch squares (to be used as the
>   blueprint for each month)
>   colored markers or pencils
>   blank white paper
>   paper punches
>   string

1) Fill in the days of the week at the top of the grid. Refer to a published calendar to fill in the days of each month.

2) For each month, make a drawing of a forest scene, appropriate for that month. (For example, a forest filled with snow would describe January, but not May.)

3) Record your observations on your calendar as well as in your journal. It's fun to look back and see what happened when!

♠ *If you like, you can "gift" your calendar in the spring or fall to those who will be studying the forest next year. This will enable them to compare events from one year to the next.*

SETON WATCH: SIT 'N WATCHES

What is a Seton Watch? This "sit and watch" experience is named after a naturalist, Ernest Thompson Seton. He learned the secrets of Mother Nature by sitting quietly, observing and listening with his ears and his heart. Since you will be sitting still for five to ten minutes outdoors, dress appropriately.

❧ During a Seton Watch, try to "feel" what's going on around you by using all your senses. To do this, you will have to be very quiet. After five to ten minutes of silent sitting, feeling, and listening, Mother Nature may reveal some almost invisible, magical details of Winter, something that would otherwise be frozen in the silence.

(continued)

What can you do while sitting still?

- Watch for insects or animals that may suddenly appear!
- Look at the frozen colors and silhouettes on the Winter landscape.
- Look for snow crystals or frost formations shimmering in the sunshine - some may appear on your coat sleeve!
- Look at Winter's shadows.
- Listen to the whispering wind.
- Listen to the questions your quiet self wants to ask.

Following a Seton Watch, you might want to draw yourself in the Winter landscape. You might also enjoy a share circle to tell friends what you discovered during your sit 'n watch.

Want To Do More?

🐾 Read aloud the **life stories of Ernest Seton**. These tales may inspire stewardship and awe of the wonders of nature. Some of Seton's favorite animals stories are found in <u>Wild Animals I Have Known.</u> Titles include Raggylug the Cottontail, Silverspot the Crow, and The Springfield Fox.

🐾 Retell your favorite stories. Or put on a short skit about Ernest Seton and the wild animals he knew.

A WINTER GUIDE TO EVERGREENS

Are there different kinds of evergreens? Do they each have a special place they like to grow?

Winter Evergreen explorations help you discover the diversity of evergreen trees and their adaptations. You can observe a single evergreen tree, or investigate a grove of evergreens growing near your Ecology Action Research Station. If there aren't any evergreen trees nearby, you can bring samples of different evergreen trees inside, with cones or berries attached.

Make your own Evergreen Identification Cards

❢ To make your own **Evergreen Identification Cards**, the following paragraphs can be photocopied, then cut individually and laminated onto index cards with clear contact paper. If you want to keep these identification key cards at the research station, store them in a protected place, such as in a large yogurt container. Be sure you understand how to key species with them. Then go out into the forest or fields and identify some trees with your key!

♠ ♠ ♠

   Look at the needles on the evergreen tree. Are they as long as fingers, wispy and found in clusters? How many needles are there in the cluster?

- **Two needles** denote the **Red Pine**.
- **Pitch Pine** has **three needle clusters**.
- **Five needles are on the White Pine**, known by Native people in the Northeast as the Tree of Peace. It is easy to remember the White Pine cluster. You can think of its five needles as spelling W-H-I-T-E or P-E-A-C-E.

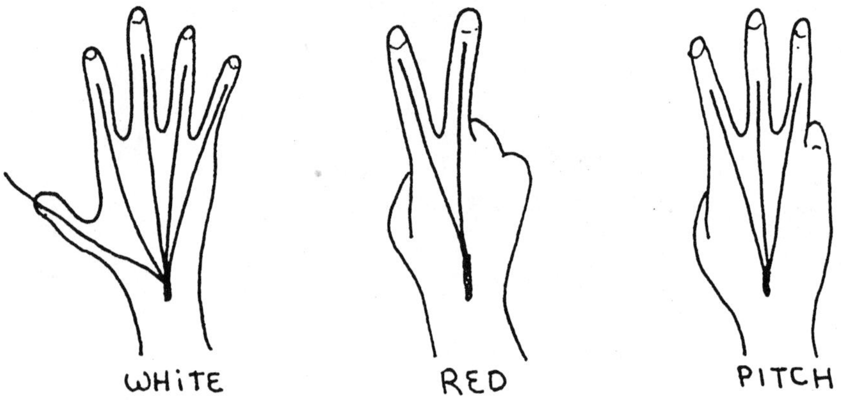

WHITE   RED   PITCH

(For reverse of card)

Ancient White Pine trees have maintained a place on the landscape since the dinosaur days. This is due to their great flexibility and special adaptations. Pine tree branches grow in whorls around the trunk and shed the weight of heavy snows in Winter. After the first four years, a new whorl of branches grows annually and the lower ones die back. How old is your tree? This strong yet gentle tree provides a shelter and feeding ground for many birds and animals. Ship masts take their wood from ancient Pine. If you stop beneath them for a moment you can enjoy their lovely scent.

(continued)

♠ ♠ ♠

Are the needles on this tree flat and irregularly shaped, resembling a feather leaf? **Cedar needles have a scale-like** texture.

(For reverse of card)

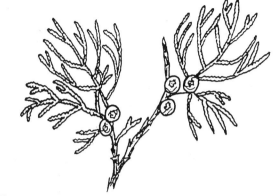

Featherleaf White Cedar

Some northeastern Native people called the White Cedar "Feather-leaf", or Oo-see-ha-tah. Its relative, the Red Cedar, has blue berries, which mice and birds love to eat.

♠ ♠ ♠

Does the tree have single, flat, regularly-spaced short needles the length of your thumbnail? Do they look the same topside and bottom? If you see white lines at the bottom of the needle, with a short stem between the needle and twig, you have found **Hemlock**. Look for tiny rosebud-shaped cones on the Hemlock branches.

Hemlock

(For reverse of card.)

The Hemlock tree lives in densely shaded forests, and its lower branches can survive for many years without direct sunlight. Rabbit and deer love to feed on these low branches. These trees are nearly 300 years old when mature, and some live to twice that age!

♠ ♠ ♠

If the lined needles have no stem at the base of the needles, and the needles are slightly rounded at the ends, you have found **Balsam Fir,** full of the smell of Christmas.

(For reverse of card)

Balsam

Balsam, also called Balm of Gilead, is a popular Christmas tree not only because of its wonderful fragrance, but because it holds its needles for a long time after the tree is cut. The light, soft, brittle wood of the Balsam fir is used for boxes and crates.

♠ ♠ ♠

Look for needles that surround the branch on all four sides. Are they are sharply pointed? Do they give a slight prick - almost like a sewing needle - when touched? Look at the bottom of the tree. Does a skirt form at the base? Meet **Spruce tree.** Its skirt allows snow to slide down so its branches won't break. The tree branches and needles form such a dense shape that they become like a tent, offering protection from the storm.

(For reverse of card)

Chewing gum was once made from Spruce tree's resin.

Spruce

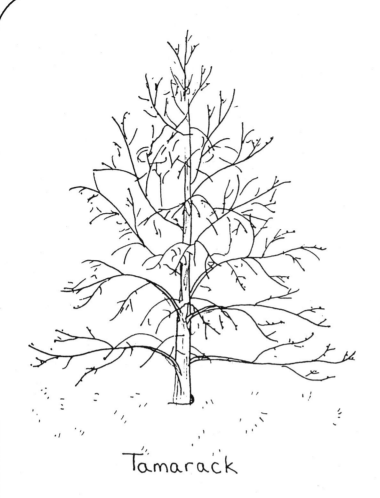

Tamarack

♠ ♠ ♠
Look for a tree silhouette that is triangular-shaped, yet reveals bare, golden or brown branches. Look below the tree for signs of deposited evergreen needles. One evergreen tree does shed its needles. It's name is **Tamarack**.

(For reverse of card)

Tamarack is also known as Larch or Hackmatack. The astringent sap was formerly used in the treatment of bronchitis and hemorrhages. It is used today, when mixed with soap and glycerine, as a local remedy for skin irritations.

Want To Do More?

  🍂 Make **rubbings** from evergreen samples. These can become lovely Winter Solstice cards, Peace cards or stationary.

  🍂 After identifying evergreen samples, secure them upright in a little ball of clay, wax, or play dough. These **miniatures** can be displayed on a nature table complete with a white cloth, moss, and sculptures of forest animals. Which evergreen holds its needles the longest?

(continued)

Math, Nature's Way:

❧ Can you find ways to use your fingers as a standard of measure?

For example:

- If you spread your fingers, how many inches does your hand measure from thumb to pinky?

- How long is your thumb from its tip to the first knuckle?

- If you stretch your hand straight out from your body, what is the distance from the tip of your nose to your fingertips?

- What is the measurement of an average step in your walking pace?

- How long is your foot?

- How tall are you?

❧ Measure some household or classroom objects, using hands, fingers, arm lengths, or a walking pace for measuring tools. If you and your friends stood on one another's shoulders, how many of you would it take to be as tall as your favorite tree? How tall would that tree be? Once you know your own body measurements, you won't have to depend on a ruler! That is, until your body grows.

WINTER'S HUSH: SNOW WALKING AND THE CIRCLE GAME

Have you ever imagined what an animal hears as it walks the Winter forest? Sometimes, when you close your eyes, your other senses become more acute. The following activity gives you the opportunity to explore some stalking techniques, with and without the use of your eyesight.

To play Winter Hush Walking:

1) Remove your shoes.
2) Hide a "mouse" somewhere in the room.
3) Have fabric or newspaper on hand.

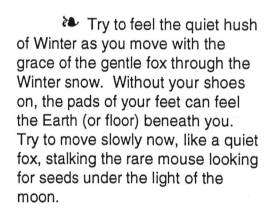

Try to feel the quiet hush of Winter as you move with the grace of the gentle fox through the Winter snow. Without your shoes on, the pads of your feet can feel the Earth (or floor) beneath you. Try to move slowly now, like a quiet fox, stalking the rare mouse looking for seeds under the light of the moon.

Search with your eyes and move quietly, so mouse does not hear you. Slowly raise one foot and place it down without a sound. Now step silently with the other. Close your eyes as you do this. Do you

hear the sound of your footstep?

♠ Now try exploring different ways to stalk. First, step down with your toes touching first. . . now step down first with your heel. . . now step down first on the side of your foot and gently roll it over 'till it all touches the ground. Which way can you be most quiet? Try to stalk all around the room as hushed as can be, listening to the quiet, the stillness of Winter. When you feel finished, silently sit down and tuck your head under your tail in your fox den, then listen to the sounds of quiet foxes.

♠ As an alternative, half the group can be still as mice with their eyes closed and their ears wide open. The rest of the group may be quiet foxes, moving about as silently as possible.

♠ If you want more of a **challenge,** scatter pieces of fabric and paper about the room. See who can stalk without making the fabric or paper sound!

✍ *Now can be a great time for* **poetry** *to grow from the hush. Record and illustrate a simple rhyme in your nature journal.*

Want To Do More?

🐾 **Try Winter Hush Walking when you are outside** after a fresh snow. While quietly walking, imagine you are an animal stalking a mouse after a Winter snowfall. First, you may like to just practice the winter hush walking method outdoors to get the feel for how animals move in deep or light snow. Later you can actually pretend to be stalking a real mouse, while searching the area for mouse tracks in the snow.

🐾 **Choose a predator, and learn its tracks.** Then familiarize yourself with the tracks of an animal it eats. To help you to identify these tracks, you may enjoy laminating pictures of them on cards. These cards can then be worn around your neck for safe-keeping and quick referral. To avoid the confusion of learning too many tracks at once, wear just the set of tracks you are working with right now. Search for signs of winter animal activity using the Winter Hush Walking method. Later when you go on more Winter Hush Walking journeys, you may use additional cards to identify any unknown tracks you discover in the snow or mud.

- Look for the types of animal tracks which have five digits front and back, just like you.

- Do any tracks include trail dragging?

- What animals seem to be searching for food in the winter forest?

- Who or what do they search for?

- What might it be like to be an animal looking for food during the Winter?

☙ It's fun to find fresh tracks in the Winter and to follow the trail of an animal in your outdoor neighborhood. Often it's only the tracks left behind and not the animal itself you see. To get a better feel for Winter animal travel, can you act like one of your favorite animals?

- Which animals are leapers, runners, walkers?

- Try to get the feel of a leaping rabbit, landing with rear feet forward and front paws in the center and a bit behind the back feet.

- Act out a fox trotting. Move your left front and back "feet" together, and your right front and back "feet" together. For a real challenge, try to place your left foot/hand in the same track as your right foot/hand.

- How might a mouse, a rabbit or a deer move in the snow?

(continued)

Even More Curious?

Winter Hush Circle Game

🕊 Play a Winter Hush Circle game. A group plays this circle game by moving sunwise, or clockwise, repeating the poem and actions while moving twice around. After you have mastered this circle game, you can try doing it once sunwise, then reversing direction for the second go round!

Spoken in swift hushed voices; soft, swift leaping footsteps:

> The foxes move so swiftly,
> They hardly make a sound,

Tiny rhythmical voice; quick, light, fluid steps scamper across floor:

> Mouse dashes 'neath the moonlight,
> Paws softly brush the ground.

Graceful voice; leap, arms and legs sailing over floor, landing with firm contact for a brief moment:

> Deer leap above their shadows,
> Springing, bounding, hooves touch down.

Pace voices like drumbeat; solid, strong rear paws land with front paws dangling slightly between and behind rear paws:

> Rabbit leaps through thicket fleet,
> Drumming Earth with strong back feet!

Math, Nature's Way

Measure your tracks in the snow, using your hands and fingers as measuring devices the same way you did in "A Winter Guide to Evergreens." Then check your estimations with a ruler.

- How wide are they?

- How long is your track?

- How far apart is each step?

- How far is the distance between the steps your left foot takes.

- Try running through the snow at different speeds. Then measure the distances between steps again.

- How do the size of your tracks change over time? Each day, go outside and measure your tracks. Why do you think they change?

THE ROTTING LOG: A WINTER FOREST TERRARIUM

What goes on in the world of a rotting log? Find an interesting piece of an old decomposing tree limb or log to study. For table top observation you can make a large terrarium, small individual terrariums, or a two-person terrarium to share with a nature friend.

> ☛ *Note:* You may find it easiest to collect the rotting log in late Fall before the snow falls. You can still gather one in Winter, although you may need a shovel to free it from the frozen earth.

To create a Winter Forest Terrarium you will need:

> a gallon jar with lid, or an old aquarium with a glass cover
> thermometer
> eighteen-, sixteen-, and ten-penny nails
> a hammer
> sand or gravel, charcoal chips, and potting soil

1) Place a one-inch layer of gravel or coarse sand for drainage in the bottom of your container. Add a thin layer of charcoal chips to absorb odor. Add some potting soil, humus, duff, dead leaves, moss or moss-covered stones, and lichen.

2) Place a rotting log inside the terrarium. Feel free to add special touches like small stones, tiny pine cones, or handmade clay creations to the rotting log village in the terrarium.

   ♠ You might find it interesting to record the temperature changes inside the log as it thaws. To do this, gently hammer a nail six inches into the log. Hammer another nail about four inches into the log, and another about two inches. Remove the nails and place thermometers in the holes. Record daily temperatures, and compare them as the log thaws.

3) Mist and cover with the jar lid or a piece of glass if you are using an old aquarium. This helps prevent moisture loss. **Keep away from direct sunlight** or your log might cook!

4) Observe your terrarium daily or you might miss some of the secret adventures of a rotting log in Winter!

✍ *In your nature journal you can draw what you see happening in the small world within your terrarium. If you share this journal with a friend, show her the terrarium too. Otherwise she might not believe all the things that are happening in the quiet world of a rotting log!*

THE ROTTING LOG: DECAY OR DELIGHT?

Did you ever wonder if a dead tree is simply something messing up the forest floor? Or is there more than meets the eye? Use your rotting log terrarium to find out.

❧ Have you always thought that trees are hard and strong? What do rotting trees feel like when you touch them? You may be surprised to feel that rotting trees can be as soft as a sponge! Rotting logs that are soft as a sponge are very soggy because they soak up rainwater that falls in the forest. This wet habitat is a good place for mosses, young ferns, and fungi to take up housekeeping. Do you see any mosses, ferns or tree fungi growing on the surface? What are they doing there? Do they look the same every day? Keep searching and examining this quiet world of the rotting log and you may discover some of the following quiet inhabitants in the rotting log terrarium!

Mosses belong to the miniature world of the plant kingdom. They are so small that it is easy to imagine them as being part of the forests of the fairy folk and gnomes. Soft green pillows and carpets can be found on rocks or stumps in dark, moist woodlands the world over. Though all the mosses may appear at first to look the same, a sharp eye will observe that these fairy pillows are quite unique.

♠ The **Hair-cap Moss** is often found growing in a forest near the Wintergreen. It may be brownish-green in Winter, and if carefully dug up may be brought indoors to become a guest in the rotting log terrarium. If it has been a dry Winter with little snow, the moss greens may be wrapped tightly around its stem to conserve moisture loss.

Look closely at the moss to see which parts of the plant are still green and growing. This year's growth is fresh and green. What do you think the drier brown parts are? They are the growth from the year before, and perhaps the year before that.

For a special treat, water a little dry part of the stem or mist it heavily. Watch it uncurl, just as it would if the rain were falling upon it!

♠ How do mosses find their way to the moist soggy places of the forest? Mosses do not grow by seed, as many other plants do. The father part of the moss is found along the end of the stem, and looks like a star-pointed cup. Older star cups from previous years may be found farther down the stem, hidden between areas of old growth. The father cells are carried on the wind to some of the plants that have mother cells. The mother parts are so tiny you cannot see them!

♠ Another name for Hair-cup moss is "Pigeon Wheat". Above the top of the mossy, pillow-like mass, you will find a flagpole-shaped structure. When the father and mother cells come together, a case that looks like a grain of wheat may emerge at the end of the flagpole stalk. Hence the name Pigeon Wheat. The wheat-grain case may be covered with a yellow fuzz, like a warm, fuzzy winter hat.

What colors and shapes do you see when you look with a hand lens at the shape of the wheat-grain case? Gently open a wheat-grain case to see what is inside. The dust found inside is actually **spores**. Instead of seeds for creating young plants, the mother part of the moss carries these dusty spores. When they are ripe, the wheat-grain vessel bows down and, like a pepper shaker, sprinkles the spores. The spores are carried on the wind to the place where they will rest and make a new home. What kind of place will they find best suited for life as a young moss?

Remember: *Be sure to keep your rotting log terrarium moist so that any spores that travel in the terrarium will find a soggy place to call home. Daily misting is recommended.*

(continued)

♠ The life of a moss begins with the mother cells, which cannot be seen because they are so tiny. The spores form in the wheat-grain case, become mature and are dropped like pepper. If the habitat is favorable, branching green threads begin to spread across the ground. Finally, over time, the green foliage of the moss forms the fairy forest. Can you draw a circle of life illustration for the moss?

Want To Do More?

❧ Mushrooms

Most mushrooms and other fungi are the forest's friends. They work with dead and dying trees to help break down wood and bark into soil. If you look closely at mushrooms, you will notice they lack the color green. Mushrooms do not make their own food as many other plants do. They survive on the green food that has been stored in the trees. Fungi and mushrooms get the nutrients they need when they break down wood and bark into soil.

You have probably heard many stories about poisonous mushrooms. It is true that some mushrooms are deadly, while other mushrooms are edible.   So never eat mushrooms you find the forest! Let the slugs and snails eat the forest mushrooms instead, as they have a keen sense of what is safe to eat.

Like the mosses, mushrooms also reproduce by spores. You can discover mushroom spores by performing the **following experiment:**

A Mushroom Surprise:

1) Carefully pick a freshly-opened mushroom and remove the stem so that only the cap remains.

2) Put the mushroom cap on a piece of white paper with the gills facing down.

3) Cover the mushroom cap with a glass, and wash your hands.

4) After 24 hours, carefully remove the mushroom cap and look at the surprise left on the paper!

♠ Note the color and shape of the imprint. Where do you think this fine dust came from?

♠ Look beneath the cap and you will find structures called **gills**. This is where the spores are stored. As a mushroom begins to dry out, it releases its spores onto the ground in the hope of creating new mushrooms.

✍ *In your nature journal, you may want to illustrate the beautiful pattern of the spores or the gills. Or illustrate one of the mushrooms growing in your rotting log terrarium.*

❧ Fungi

Bracket fungi grow on the side of the tree and resemble a shelf for the wee people of the forest. One type of bracket fungi often found on dying wood is pearly white, soft and shiny. These sturdy, white bracket fungi are fun to sketch on. Use a toothpick or sharp pencil to sketch your forest scene. Shortly after being etched into the fungus, the sketch lines will discolor and become brown. Save your fungus etching and make them a permanent record of your nature notes.

The **Scarlet Saucer** is another type of tree fungi. It lives on rotting branches buried in leaf litter on the forest floor. This bowl-like, fungus grows from a nubby stem. The outside of the Scarlet Saucer is a light color and feels soft, like skin. The inside of the saucer is brown to scarlet and rather bristly feeling, like a stubby beard.

As already noted, bracket fungi also survive on dead wood. There are other fungi species that survive on living trees. Some of these fungi weaken the tree, making it susceptible to harmful fungi or diseases which may kill it. But not all fungi that survive on living trees harm them.

❧ Lichen

Pixie cups are gray-green goblets, just the right size for a tiny dew drop. These miniature table settings are less than a half inch tall - perfect for a Pixie.

Soldier's Caps are as tiny as pixie cups, but their bright red color - a sharp contrast against the green forest floor - commands attention. Look closely at this fascinating character. Notice their red caps, sitting on delicate green stalks. These caps are similar to the hats worn by British soldiers - hence the name Soldier's Caps.

Lichen is a very unusual plant. In fact, it is actually <u>two</u> plants in one! These two plants, an algae and a fungus, live cooperatively. This marvelous way of working together is known as **symbiosis**. The fungus holds the plant to the stone or wood surface, thereby providing a safe home for the algae. It also soaks up moisture, like a sponge. In return, the **algae** produces food. It takes a long time for these slow-growing pioneer plants to develop. Though able to endure rugged conditions, lichen are very sensitive to pollution.

♠ *Can you make up a story about the wee folk of the forest who live among mushrooms, fungi, and pixie cups?*

❧ Leaf Litter

Look at the mat of leaves under your rotting log. This **duff**, as it is called, may not look like much at first, but it is home to many of the smaller inhabitants of the forest. Some of these critters are so tiny they are almost invisible! If you carefully separate some of the leaves, you might discover something hidden within them.

Some leaves may be well preserved. Do you know which tree they come from? Do any of the decaying leaves look like skeletons? Separate the leaves gently to see if all of them look the same.

Try making a time line of leaves. Begin the time line with the leaf that is the most preserved and whole. End the time line with the leaf that is the most decayed, the one that has changed the most. What story do these leaves tell? The leaves show the process of changing from solid matter to fine humus.

Look in the leaf litter for earthworms, insects and germinating seeds. Invisible forest inhabitants also live in the leaf litter. Thousands of micro-organisms work with the worms to help change the leaf litter into rich humus.

Illustrate what you discovered about the leaf litter in your nature journal. When you return the leaf litter blanket to the terrarium, place it beneath the rotting log until your next discovery check-in.

Remember: When caring for your rotting log terrarium, remember that micro-organisms work better if the leaf litter is kept moist by daily misting.

❧ Ferns

While studying a rotting log terrarium, it might be fun to bring in ferns from the local garden shop. Ferns require low to moderate light and are a perfect way to green up a dull corner in Winter. Examine the different shapes of their fronds. Look for spore cases. Newly-developing fronds are fun to watch - observe them as they uncurl!

EXPLORING THE ROTTING LOG COMMUNITY

Is a dead tree more than simply forest litter? As you've probably discovered, an entire miniature world exists in a very tiny place!

🐦 You might enjoy **displaying the terrarium** on a nature table in a quiet, dark corner. Light a candle behind it to illuminate the inhabitants within and to help create a quiet atmosphere for observation.

Liven up the display by making some watercolor paintings of the rotting log terrarium. Hang the paintings in the nature corner. Watch what happens in the rotting log community over the next weeks to come.

♠ In order to observe the rotting log, carefully remove it **once a week**. Illustrate any changes of appearance in odor, texture, color, emerging plants, or critters who live there. What cooperation do you observe among the inhabitants? What do they share in common?

♠ After several days of a quiet "getting to know you" time with your rotting log community, choose **inhabitants of the week** to focus on, such as mushrooms, fungi, leaf litter, lichen, ferns or insects. Sculpt the inhabitants of your terrarium from beeswax or other modeling material.

♠ **Observe the terrarium daily** with a hand lens or a large insect-magnifying box.

♠ **Write a poem** about the plants and animals that dwell within the rotting log. Illustrate your favorite inhabitant and **write a story** about it.

♠ If you've always thought of trees as great, hard objects, you are in for a surprise! **Feel the texture** of the rotting log.

♠ After five or six weeks of observation, you might want to **take the rotting log apart** to observe the hidden inhabitants and wonders that lie within. Do this with great care, though, as an unexpected guest may surprise you! Are there masses of thread-like roots within? Even before a tree becomes part of the forest soil, other plant roots seek out its supply of minerals. Next, can you find the walls of this tree before parts of it decayed? Feel for a rope-like or string-like material inside. This rope-like cellulose is all that is left of the tree's walls.

🐛 What do you think? Is a "dead tree" more than simply forest litter? Is a dead tree decay, or delight? As you've probably discovered, a dead tree makes **tree-mendous** contributions to the forest long after its growing days have ended! It continues to "give away" its nutrients, providing a banquet table for many diverse and amazing animals and plants! How can something that is dead add value to the world? Name a few things a dead tree can do.

🐛 You might enjoy **creating a story** about the "Old Ones" who are decaying in our forests. What stories do they have to tell about the passing of time?

Want To Do More?

🐛 It might be fun to **compare** the inhabitants of a Deciduous Forest Rotting Log terrarium with the inhabitants of an Evergreen Forest Rotting Log terrarium.

🐛 You can culminate your observations by creating a larger-than-life **diorama** of a rotting log. Make a large, stand-up tree from cardboard. Cut an opening in the trunk large enough to peek through. Look inside to observe the friendly forest inhabitants that live in a rotting tree! Consider sculpting, drawing, modeling, or even making a mural to celebrate the life of a rotting log. Place each display in a corrugated cardboard box attached to the back of the tree behind the peep hole, or hang it from a wall behind the tree.

WAKE UP, LITTLE CREATURES, WAKE UP!
WHO'S BEEN FROZEN IN THAT ROTTING LOG?

Did you find little creatures as well as plants living in your Rotting Log Community? Sometimes, inactive inhabitants emerge from their winter sleep. If you are lucky, you might discover some hidden critters. . . .

🐌 You might find a single-legged animal living in your rotting log terrarium. Look carefully for the camouflaged spiral shell of the hibernating **forest snail**. This slow-moving fellow hibernates in the winter between the leaf litter and the rotting log. Sometimes a hibernating **woodland toad** shares the protection of the rotting log with the forest snail.

🐌 Other inhabitants might include the thousand-legged, or **millipede,** and the hundred-legged, the **centipede**. Do you see any? Actually, if you were to count the legs of these two insects you would find that they don't live up to their names. Centipedes are very quick-moving creatures that search for slugs, insects and worms to eat. A centipede's flat body is great for sneaking under bark and stones, which enables them to seek for hidden food in the damp darkness. They sometimes pinch when threatened by curious hands, so treat these many-legged creatures with respect!

🐌 **Millipedes**, on the other hand, resemble worms that have too many legs - in fact, they can hardly move with all those legs! These ungainly vegetarians inhabit the leaf litter and soil layers. Instead of pinching you with poison claws, millipedes curl into a tight ball when a giant hand threatens them. If you really aggravate a millipede, they might emit a stinky fluid. The fluid is an **adaptation** of this crawling pacifist.

🐌 Do you see any small, gray, oval-shaped creatures, known as **pillbugs** or **sowbugs** or **rolly-polies**? These critters are called pillbugs because if you touch one it rolls up into a pill-size shape for protection. To see if this creepy crawly thing is really a pillbug, gently touch one. If it is a pillbug, the next question you might ask is, is it really a bug? Count the legs to find out. True bugs have a triangular shield on their backs. Check for this identifying shape on the pillbug.

🐛 Other tiny creatures you might find include **insect eggs** of bees, wasps, and crickets. If you see a fast-moving flash of red the size of a pinhead, you've met the rotting log inhabitant known as **Mite**.

🐛 Other insect inhabitants that actually live in a rotting log can include **wood ants, stag beetles** and **stag larva, ground beetles, earwigs** (which also like to pinch), **springtails,** even **silk cases of pupating moths** or **butterflies**. Is anybody home?

Remember to look closely at a rotting log outside during the spring thaw. Do you think you will see any of the same creatures that emerged in your rotting log terrarium?

THE INDOOR FOREST

You may already have an indoor tree, but a single tree doesn't make a forest! The best way to get to know a forest is to visit one. However, if there are few trees where you live, an indoor forest can provide enjoyment. Design an indoor forest that looks, smells, sounds and feels like a real forest!

Some ideas to get you started:

🍂 You will need a **variety of tree samples** for your indoor forest. You may harvest, with care, some young trees from the forest. Find an area where saplings are growing closely together, and choose some that look as if they could use some thinning. Remember to thank the tree spirits!

🍂 **Support your saplings** in Christmas tree stands or in buckets filled with stones. You can also make a wooden tree stand by nailing two 2x4 scraps into the shape of an "X". Anchor the tree base into the center of the X with 18-penny nails or a lug bolt. If you don't want to cut down live trees from the forest, remove a young tree seedling - but be careful to keep all of its roots intact. Bring it back to the classroom and make it part of your living indoor forest. Remember to plant it in a sunny area in the spring! .

🍂 To enhance your forest atmosphere, gather **nuts, pine cones, fallen bark from trees or wood piles,** even **mossy stones.** If you bring bark or stones that are covered with lichen or mosses indoors, remember to mist them regularly.

🍂 Collect treasures like **bones, tree fungus, nests, feathers, rocks, owl pellets** or **snake skins** and put them in the indoor forest exhibit. Arrange these special effects so they look at home in your indoor forest.

🍂 Complete your indoor forest by filling it with special **sound effects.** Create your own instruments and vocal forest symphony of whispering pines, mourning doves, ruffed grouse drumming, owl calls or foxes yelping. Or record your own environmental "sounds of the forest" tape in the great outdoors, and see how many sounds your friends can identify!

🍂 Keep a **mystery bag** in the indoor forest. Each day you can place a different object from the forest into the bag. Members of the class can take turns reaching in to feel and identify the objects.

🍂 For an interesting sensory experience, try **"mystery smells of the forest".** Collect some baby food jars and fill them with different forest materials - such as decomposing leaves, pine needles, or wintergreen leaves. Punch holes in the lids, or cover the jar with fabric and secure it with a rubber band.

(continued)

🍂 **Each week explore different animals of the Winter forest.** What does each animal need for shelter, food, protection, warmth? What special qualities do you enjoy about different forest animals? What can you learn from your fur-covered friends?

🍂 Learn more about forest animals through read-aloud chapter books, such as the story of <u>Hugh Pine</u>, the porcupine. <u>Fantastic Mr. Fox</u> is a humor-filled adventure about a sly fox who tries to outsmart the local hen-house keepers. In his humorous children's story called <u>Owls in the Family</u>, Farley Mowat shares some of his knowledge about owls, as well as sharing his concerns about the wisdom of keeping wildlife for pets. Look in the bibliography for further information.

🍂 Find out what happens to animals that are inactive in Winter, such as ovenbirds, chipmunks, snails, gypsy moths and salamanders.

🍂 With a hand lens, or simply a pair of curious eyes, **observe** the special characteristics of your indoor forest tree samples, bark, lichens, mosses, fungus, fallen leaves and nuts. You can give the trees in your indoor forest creative names. Or use identification guides as a key to their identities.

GRANDFOREST TREE TELLS A STORY

If you could understand the language of the animals, think of the tales they could tell! But listen - for Grandforest Tree knows their language. He can tell you many stories, for he is very old and very wise.

"Why Squirrel Hops Between the Trees"

Once, long ago, when my great-great-great-great grandfather was beginning to grow tall in the Big Woods that grew here, Squirrel had wings and could fly. She flew all through the forest, taunting rabbits and mice with her obnoxious chatter. She often stole nuts and seeds from the mice or chipmunks. She was not well liked and had few friends.

"As winter approached, Squirrel was scurrying around, stealing yummy things from others and storing them to eat in the cold of Winter. She was very greedy and had large caches of food hidden everywhere. Since she could fly well, she traveled great distances to get the choicest nuts and seeds in the forest.

"Winter came early one year, before many of the animals had finished gathering enough to eat. As the cold months wore on, many feared starvation. Squirrel only made things worse by terrorizing those who had worked hard to gather food. Sometimes she swooped down on an unsuspecting animal and stole its meal! Worse, her bird's-eye view enabled her to see other animals' food storage places, and she often raided their caches. When the animals asked her to stop, she teased them with a loud 'Churrrrrrrrrrrr!!'

"One day, the animals awoke to snow falling. It snowed all day, filling the woods with wondrous white fluff. For days it snowed and snowed. This was good news for the animals

157

because they knew the insulating snow-blanket would keep them warm. Squirrel, however, was not pleased. She could no longer see the animals' dining rooms because everything was hidden beneath the snow! And she could no longer find her own caches, as they were also hidden. The familiar landmarks she had used to locate her storage places had disappeared.

"Squirrel flew down to the ground and poked around for fallen seeds. The hard, white silence moved in on her. She started to feel lonely, for the other animals were snug in their burrows. What could she do now that there was no one to tease or steal food from? How would she find food? She began to fear for her life. The North Wind began to blow snow in cold swirls, singing bitter songs of ice and frost. Shivering, Squirrel tried to bury herself in a snowdrift. After a time she began to feel warmer, thanks to the layers of snow. Soon she fell into a deep sleep, but she had a fearful dream.

"In her dream she had no wings, and had to hop about on four legs like the other animals of the forest. She was busily munching on some delectable pine nuts when ferocious Hawk came down and stole the pine cone right out of her paws! Squirrel was furious! She had saved that pine cone all Winter, wanting to eat it on this day - which happened to be her birthday. To make matters worse, Hawk mocked her from the top of a tall pine. Squirrel tried to scold her, but Hawk continued to laugh. Then Hawk flew down and, with her huge talons, gently picked up Squirrel. Hawk set her down on top of a nest of sticks.

"'Who do you think you are, stealing my food?' asked Squirrel, who was furious but terrified.

"'Who do you think YOU are?' answered Hawk. 'You do the same to others. But I am here to teach you a lesson,' she said. 'For I am Queen of all the forest animals, and I will not tolerate your behavior any longer. You were given the gift of flight, but

you have abused that gift. First, you will lose your wings. Second, you will be forced to search for and store your own food. Finally, if you ever steal from anyone ever again, I will scoop YOU up for a meal!'

"Hawk's eyes blazed, and Squirrel understood she was serious about everything she said.

"'I will do as you say,' Squirrel said humbly. 'I will forage for my own food, and not steal from others. But how can I live on the ground with the others if I have no friends?'

"Hawk replied, 'Oh, you will have friends, but you will have to work hard at making them. You must find a way to make yourself useful.' With that, Hawk took wing and flew away. And Squirrel found herself alone, without wings to fly down from the tree.
"Squirrel awoke suddenly, startled. Had she been dreaming, or was it real? Where was she? All was white around her. Then she remembered. She was snuggled in a snowdrift. It had only been a dream after all! But as she struggled out of the snow, she realized that her wings were gone. And so was most of the snow! So it wasn't a dream!

"Squirrel thought about this, and for a long while she was very sad. She had loved to fly - what would life be like without wings? A heavy sigh escaped her. But at last she thought, Oh, well, at least it will be easier to find food.

"But then a new thought troubled her. If she were to make friends, she needed to make herself useful. But how? Suddenly, she saw a hungry Fox looking for a meal. Realizing she couldn't simply fly away anymore, she quickly climbed a tree, and from her high perch scolded the intruder with as loud a 'CHURRRRR!' as she could muster. Instantly, all the other little animals took cover, thinking that the nasty little Squirrel-bird was about to steal their food. But then they realized what she was doing - she had saved their lives by warning them about the Fox!

"When they felt safe enough, the animals scrambled from their hiding places to thank Squirrel. To their amazement, she no longer had wings! They cheered her boldness with Fox, and gathered around her as though she were a heroine. As Squirrel stood proudly among them, the animals welcomed her to share the ground with them.

"So whenever you walk in the woods now, you will likely hear the insistent chatter of Squirrel, warning the others of your presence. And since Squirrel can no longer fly, she hops between trees - look for her tracks in the snow!"

READING THE WINTER WOODS FOR ANIMAL SIGNS

It's a rare day when animals reveal themselves to hikers. But if you learn how to look for signs of animal presence, you can tell who's been where - and when.

Some Things to Look for:

🐾 Keep an eye out for **woodpecker holes.** Sometimes squirrels store acorns there.

🐾 If you look up very high, you may see **bark eaten off a pine tree.** A porcupine probably did that. Check for porcupine quills around the tree. If there is snow, his wandering path may show where he waddled between his den and the trees.

🐾 Near water, you may see **tree trunks that have been chewed** through or felled. If the trees are chewed in a triangular or hourglass shape, it is the sign of a beaver's work. Check for teeth marks on the chewed area, and collect some "beaver chips" - wooden shavings from the gnawed tree.

🐾 **Check under logs for stored seeds.** This is the work of squirrels and chipmunks. These quick critters also hide their food underground, so look for places where the earth has been disturbed. When snow covers the ground, squirrel excavations are especially obvious. Look for scattered pine cone debris near holes!

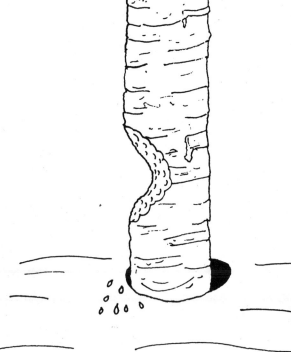

🍂 If you find **grasses nibbled** to the ground, it may mean a rabbit has been grazing.

🍂 Grazing deer often dine on **Sumac fruits**. Look for nibbled berries on Sumac's furry branches.

🍂 Examine the ground beneath trees for signs of **littered tree bark**. A woodpecker may have dropped her lunch there!

🍂 **A stone or stump that is covered with pine cone leftovers** is evidence of a hungry squirrel.

🍂 **Zigzagging road maps under a tree's bark** are probably the work of engraver or bark beetles.

🍂 **Pupa cases snuggled against a tree's bark** are probably cradling moths or baby spiders.

🍂 **Piles of scat** left behind by fox, deer or rabbit indicate that you have stumbled upon some of their favorite places.

🍂 **Tracks** left in fresh snow or mud have a lot to tell!

If you find signs of animal life, be sure to stop and show your hiking friends, as almost everyone is interested in the secret life of a forest! And don't forget to leave this magical place as you found it. Then the next person can discover some winter woodland magic, too.

Math, Nature's Way

Measure animal tracks the same way you measured your own tracks. Measure **size** (length, width), **stride** (the distance between tracks) and **straddle** (the width between tracks). Straddle gives you a sense of how wide the animals is. Follow the track to see if the animal's gait changes. How does the distance between steps change as the animal goes faster or slower?

SLEEPING BEAUTIES: THE SNOWY BLANKET OF REST

Remember how Sleeping Beauty lay seemingly lifeless in a state of frozen sleep, only to be awakened by the touch of the prince's lips? Many of the woodland beauties lie in this same frozen state, awaiting the warm kiss of Spring's light on the forest floor.

🐾 On a winter hike, search for sleeping beauties, which were once in full sight during your Autumn forest hikes. Which plants lie hidden beneath the ground? What do you think has happened to them? Leaves that dressed the flowers and shrubs throughout Summer and Fall died off during Winter, for they were unable to draw up water from the frozen earth. Winter is a time of rest for these ground-loving plants, just as it is a time of rest for deciduous trees, which shed their leaves in Autumn.

On your hike, look for forest plants in their Winter Wear. Beneath the snow you may find some "ever-green" plants. The Evergreen Fern or **Christmas Fern** remains green all Winter. It is easy to identify. Look for a leaflet on the fern. Each leaflet is shaped like a Christmas stocking. Does the fern seem tough and somewhat leathery? This waxy-type coat protects it each Winter.

Another plant to look for is called **Wintergreen**. That's probably because its deep green, shiny oval leaves remain green in Winter. You may see Wintergreen leaves sticking up above the snow, three leaves to a cluster, possibly with a dry, red berry dangling beneath the leaves. When you break a leaf in half, it smells like wintergreen gum. Edible and safe to chew, it is a wonderful breath freshener!

Goldthread is a three-leafed plant that resembles a Strawberry plant's ridged leaves. A sure way to identify it is to scratch away the soil surrounding the root. You will see a skinny gold root, slim as a thread. Hence the fitting name, Goldthread!

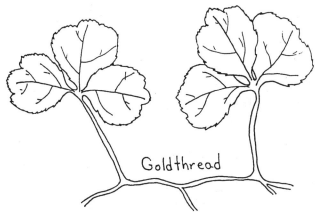

Goldthread

The **Lycopodium family** abounds on the forest floor. This small, delicate family of mosses cushions the forest floor. Its flat-topped, fan-shaped spray of scaly leaves appears to be a miniature evergreen. It is called Princess, or Ground Pine, even though it resembles a Cedar tree. However, its scaly leaves do the same work as the leaves of the Cedar - they resist moisture loss. Lycopodium is known for its healing properties and is used in remedies.

The **Club Mosses** are more lush and have a softer texture than Lycopodium. They tend to hug the earth in pillow-like clusters, gently nuzzling a lone rock here and there. Look closely at their tiny leaves, which resemble stars stacked upon one another. How does something so delicate resist freezing?

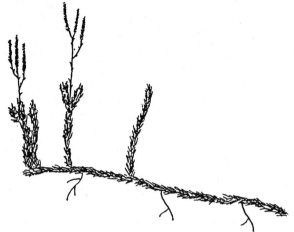

Several of the wintering forest plants have medicinal value. How nice that these plants remain visible in the Winter months, when we might need them!

Want To Do More?

🐛 List all the questions you have about these plants and their ability to survive winter. Further investigation with a naturalist or elder may help you find some answers to your questions.

🐛 What keeps the underground part of the plant from freezing? Many of the woodland wildflowers have a large, fleshy **bulb or tuber** beneath the ground that stores food for next Spring's growth. Nestled in the Earth, this mother part of the plant lies protected, awaiting the warming rays of Spring.

🐛 Try **forcing Narcissus bulbs** indoors and you will see how bulbs store food. Although they are often stored in Nature's - or your own - refrigerator, they can still grow! Put the narcissus bulbs in your refrigerator for four weeks, then remove them. Place the bulbs on some gravel that has water just below the top layer of stones. Keep the bulbs out of intense sunlight as they grow, and observe the bulbs for the next four weeks. Why didn't the bulbs bloom in the fridge? Why did they bloom when you took them out?

🐦 Snow provides a protective, insulating blanket. Just as a quilt keeps you warm at night, snow keeps small plants safe and warm by trapping air between ice crystals. Small animals burrow beneath the snow because it warms them as well.

🐦 Try the **following experiment** in the shade or on a cloudy day:

How Warm Is Snow?

Using an outdoor thermometer, take the temperature on top of a <u>shaded</u> patch of snow for five minutes. Then, make a tunnel beneath the snow and slide the thermometer in for five minutes.

Where is it warmer? How does this affect wintering plants and animals?

WINTER WEAR FOR TREES

How do trees and woodland plants adapt to the rhythms of Nature? On a hike observe evergreens, deciduous trees and woodland plants in their winter survival mode.

🌺 **How do trees protect themselves against the cold?**

Deciduous trees draw their life force inside. Humans gather around the fireside for warmth and shelter. We put on layers of clothing, while some trees seem to take them off. Trees actually save their lives by shedding leaves. When their leaves are gone, sap can't rise up through the tree. If it did, the tubes in the tree might freeze, expand and burst - as frozen pipes sometimes do in our homes! Look for trees that have shed their leaves for Winter.

Evergreen trees keep their needles all Winter. How do evergreens survive if they don't drop their needles? Look for the **waxy coating** on their needles. This waxy layer helps the trees retain water and protects them from the cold. Evergreens also produce a substance similar to antifreeze, which keeps their sap flowing smoothly. Although they continue to make food, evergreens decline into a restful state during Winter. They put their energy into general maintenance, rather than into growth.

What do you notice about the **shape** of different conifer (evergreen) trees? Which ones have a formation that allows the snow to slide off? Triangular-shaped conifer trees have special sliding ramps that hold the snow until it gets too heavy, and then let it cascade to the ground. Paper Birches also have the ability to withstand heavy snows. Instead of breaking, they bend under heavy snows. Next time you take a walk in the woods, look for these graceful brothers arcing over the trail. Other trees do not have this adaptation. A heavy snow may put so much pressure on them that they break.

Conifer branches also shelter the ground beneath them from snow. This is why animals, especially deer, take refuge under them. And although this heavy snow may not be good for every tree, it's good for wintering plants, as well as burrowing critters who make tunnels to escape their predators. **Winter snows provide a warm blanket**, protecting trees and perennial plants through the Winter. When the snow melts, it becomes the Summer's ground water.

WINTER WONDERLAND FOR RENT

Where do all the creatures of the Forest live in Winter? Take a Winter Wonderland Hike to search for the dwellings of forest inhabitants. Bring along a miniature sign reading "Winter Wonderland for Rent" and post it at a location where you think a winter inhabitant might reside. The following "advertisement" might make a nice warm-up before setting out.

"FOR RENT: WINTER WONDERLAND"

A cozy little cottage
Waits beyond the welcome door,
Soft, green, mossy pillows
Are scattered across the floor.
Oak leaves make a carpet,
Sunbeams warm the forest air,
The pantry holds the acorns
That are scattered here and there.

Moonlight mist and diamond stars
Weave a rooftop made of sky,
Moth and fireflies pay a visit
From their dreamy world up high.

Any nook or cranny
Can be suited very well,
For forest guest or resident -
Fox, Crystal, Owl or Snail.
To make your home here is so simple
Just inquire now within,

A Winter Wonderland for rent?
It's yours - so move on in.

Choose a canopy with starlights,
Where sunshine warms you on the limb,
Or settle down 'neath crystalline blankets,
In burrows cool and dim.
Behind a door of bark,
No window lets day in.
Or vacation in a squirrel nest,
If you can stand the din!

All rest soundly. Dream of Spring here,
While you're kept in Winter's care.
But be forewarned! This place will vanish,
When Spring's breath is in the air.

J.D.

🐦 As you search for the **hidden dwellings** of forest creatures on your Winter Wonderland Hike, look for holes in trees, tracks, scat, half-eaten nutshells, chewed buds or bark, burrows, and treetop nests. Also, look for piles of earthworms snuggled undercover, moss-covered tree bark, roosts for the evening owl, a drumming log for the grouse, or silky sleeping bags full of pupa resting beneath the tree bark. You might be amazed at what you find in the frozen silence of the Winter forest!

(continued)

Paint **"A Tree is an Apartment House" mural** to accompany the "Winter Wonderland for Rent" poem, or write and illustrate your own, original "Winter Wonderland For Rent" advertisement. Some homes might include a winter nursery (hidden beneath tree roots) for hidden insect young, leaf nests for squirrels, a tree hollow for a raccoon family, or chipmunk burrows beneath tree roots.

Want To Do More?

Bring **mysterious objects** back from the Winter Wonderland hike. Display them on a Winter Wonderland nature table, where you can explore them in more detail.

> ☛ *Note:* What guidelines should you establish for gathering and caring for nature objects? Here are some suggestions. If you bring back moss and lichen-covered rocks, you must be aware that they need regular misting to keep them moist. Return natural objects to their original locations when you finish with them. That way you will remain in good standing with your nature neighbors!

WINTER WONDERLAND SCAVENGER HUNT

Bundle up on a dreary day and challenge your knowledge of the Winter forest on an exciting scavenger hunt!

&❧ There are two different ways to list the objects you will gather on your scavenger hunt. Either make up a check list of Winter Wonderland treasures, or display the objects to be found. Provide gathering baskets or bags for each scavenger or team of scavengers.

Some Winter Wonderland treasures to look for:

White Pine needles
Red Pine needles
Spruce bough
Pine Cone
Hemlock Cone
Lichen
Moss
Pixie Cups
Evergreen Christmas Fern
Birch bark or other tree barks
Wintergreen or teaberry leaf
Dried Beech leaf
Hickory nut
Beech nut case
Rotting Log
Bark Beetle designs
Animal tracks
Animal Scat
Owl Pellets
Something that makes you smile
Something that smells good
Something a fairy might make use of
Something you never saw before
Golden acorn (painted by the fairy folk)
A crystal (given by the friendly gnomes)

Before you begin:

♠ Agree upon clear boundaries as well as guidelines for foraging and harvesting objects in the forest. Remind scavengers that they are guests of the forest dwellers. They should not run or act rudely in the nature neighbor's neighborhood.

♠ Determine the groupings and time limits for the hunt

♠ Distribute the treasure list or display treasures for duplication

♠ Distribute gathering baskets or treasure bags

♠ Determine what "call" will be used to notify all scavengers to return to the designated starting place.

After the hunt is complete:

♠ Share and identify the forest treasures you found on the scavenger hunt.

♠ Treasures may be returned to the forest following the hunt. Where appropriate, they can be kept and pressed into nature journals, or be kept in a shoe box diorama lined with colorful tissue paper. You may enjoy sculpting tiny forest creatures to complement the natural diorama scenery.

♠ Organize your collection into **symmetrical** and **non-symmetrical** groups. What makes something symmetrical?

FOREST CAFÉS: WILDLIFE FEEDING STATIONS

Did you ever wonder who is active in a Winter forest? Find out by opening a Wildlife Feeding Station. Attracting wildlife is easy in the Winter because animals who are out and about are looking for something to eat!

🐦 What animals do you think are active, or not hibernating, during the Winter? **Design wildlife cafés** to feed these active animal neighbors. Use recyclable containers, such as milk and cider jugs, or use twigs and lumber scraps. Avoid metal because little bird feet and tiny paws or tongues might stick to the frosty surface - just like wet fingers stick to a frozen ice cube tray! (If this has never happened to you, just try it.)

🐦 **Stock the forest cafés** using leftover scraps from lunches. Some examples of tasty morsels that will attract wildlife are stale bagels, apple cores, birdseed, or pine cones covered with suet or peanut butter. Keep the cafés well supplied and you should not be disappointed. Even city folk can attract some furry friends in Winter by setting up a café near a tree that is protected by shrubs or tall grasses.

🐦 **Make daily observations** at the forest cafés to see what has been eaten. **Record-keeping** charts may be designed to record the type of food most often eaten.

🐦 **Weigh and measure** the amount of food consumed in a day, week or month. Each day for a week or two, record the amount of food you put out. Weigh and measure what is left over before you put out more food. Subtract to find out how much food was eaten. It might be interesting to see if consumption habits change as Winter moves into Spring and animals became more active. **Graph** the amount of food eaten over the Winter.

(continued)

🐦 **Observe tracks and scat** of animals who have come and gone from your forest café.

Want To Do More?

🐦 Look for signs of active animals who browse near your café, but who may not actually eat the food. These wary visitors might include porcupine, mouse, woodpecker, deer, rabbit or owl.

♠ **Porcupine's** browsings consist of large areas of peeled bark high in the tree and tree bark litter fallen as scraps to the earth below.

♠ **Rabbit's** two front teeth are long and leave a scraping that looks exactly like two long teeth marks. Look for these marks on low branches and on the stems of shrubby growth.

♠ **Woodpeckers** actively search for insects and cocoons hidden beneath dead tree bark. Again, look up for holes, and down for fallen bark scraps near the base of the tree.

♠ **Owls** love the pines and evergreen shelter of the Winter forest. A special bundle remains after an owl feasts on the forest's menu. Look at the base of an evergreen tree for a small gray bundle of fur with specks of white crumbs, which are actually the bones of its dinner. This **owl pellet** was coughed up by an owl who swallowed its prey whole but who did not care for the fluff and bones that came with it! Carefully pull apart this pellet of fur and bones and see what else you discover. You just might find the remains of a mouse!

HAPPY VALENTINE'S DAY TO THE TREES

This year, send a Valentine to a tree! Valentine's Day can be an occasion to rejoice in the gifts trees give us.

You will need:

tree foods, such as:
    maple syrup
    fruits
    nuts
    cocoa
    teas
    coffees
    almond butter
red construction paper
fern fronds
glue
string

♥ **Decorate the room** for a Valentine party. Look around to identify Gifts from the Trees. Hang a heart-shaped note on desks, pencils, rulers, or paper that reads: "Trees Are My Friends". What might life be like without "gifts" from the trees? How does it feel when someone gives you a gift? What would you like to do in return for the gifts that trees give you?

♥ **Celebrate Valentine's Day** with food from the trees. How do trees feed us? A display of gifts from the trees might include nuts, maple syrup, teas, fruits, or cocoa. Try cooking with tree products like maple syrup, butternuts or walnuts. Or make almond butter. Serve a Valentine Day's snack made of a tree product to your friends.

♥ **Make Valentine cards** on homemade paper by using fern fronds shaped as hearts! For color, glue a tiny pressed flower at the point inside the heart. Fern fronds are also available at the local flower shop. Be sure to send some of these Valentine cards to members of your community who do not attend your celebration.

♥ Take a hike and visit your tree friends. Give them a Valentine's Day hug. Pay attention to the interesting characteristics that make each tree unique, such as bark texture and color, moss or lichen, insect holes, patterns of limbs against the sky, leaf shapes, and animal nests.

🍃 **Make a heart-shaped pouch or envelope out of birch bark as a Valentine gift:**

1) Cut two pieces of birch bark into identical heart shapes. With a hole punch, make holes for stitching the two hearts together. Leave the top of the heart open.

2) Using a large needle, stitch the bark envelope together with raffia or thick thread.

3) If you would like to hang this heart pouch, make a handle by braiding three pieces of raffia together. Attach the ends of the braids to the top hole on each side of the heart envelope.

4) You can stuff this heart pouch with Winter greens and dried berries, or embellish it with a bright red bow. The recipient of this wonderful holiday gift will be pleased by the special Valentine message you send inside it, and may enjoy using the pouch to hold mail.

WINTER TREE ART PROJECTS
BIRCHBARK CONTAINERS, GRATITUDE HOOPS, PINE CONE FIRE-STARTERS, CARDS, STATIONERY

You can develop an appreciation for the diverse and beautiful gifts from the trees throught any of the following art and craft projects.

Some Winter Tree Art suggestions:

🍂 **Birch Bark Containers** can be made by wrapping moist, flexible birch bark around tin cans. To hold the bark securely around the can, wrap the top and bottom with colorful yarn, raffia or cotton crochet string. This simple birch container can be used as a pencil holder. Or put winter greens and berries in the vase. The vase can also hold branches that you want to force indoors.

For a more challenging design:

1) Ornamental strips of bark may be used as loops in place of yarn to hold the large piece of birch bark around the can. Cut two, inch-wide birch bark strips with pinking shears to create a wave-like pattern on the edges. You might also try edging the bark with triangles or some other pleasing pattern.

2) You might find it helpful to temporarily wrap the middle of the can with a rubber band to hold the large piece of bark in place.

or,

1) Using a frozen orange juice container,glue the bark in place and hold the strips in place with rubber bands until the glue dries.

2) Attach the bark strips to the upper and lower parts of the container with rubber bands as well.

3) With a nail, hammer two holes through the top of the orange juice container where the bark layers overlap. Make two more holes in the middle and near the bottom of the container.

(continued)

4) Stitch the bark strip loops and the bark strips to the can by sewing along the seam with a sharp needle and raffia or thick thread through the holes you made.

❧ **Gratitude Hoops** are Native American expressions of appreciation for the gifts and blessings of nature. Which gifts do you wish to acknowledge during the upcoming New Year? To make a gratitude hoop that expresses your appreciation for nature's gifts, follow the directions below.

1) Begin by soaking willow, grapevine, or evergreens so that they can be bent to form a hoop. Tie the hoop branches securely together with some inconspicuous string or wire.

2) Choose some nature objects to suspend from your hoop. The objects you choose may have a special significance for you, your family, or a group you belong to. They might possess certain qualities that you wish to focus on in the coming year. For example, hang feathers that remind you of the joys your feathered friends bring you when you feed them during the Winter. Suspend a golden star from the center of the hoop as a reminder that the night's guiding lights will help you find your way through the dark Winter. Pine cones might remind you to plant a seed for future generations in thanks for Mother Nature's bounty.

3) Hang the Gratitude Hoop where you can see it. The significance of the hoop will become clearer as you ponder what the objects mean to you. You might wish to use the hoop in a ritual to celebrate and affirm significant events in your life.

❧ **Pine Cone Fire Starters** are a welcome gift in the Winter for any family who heats with wood.

1) Gather pine cones.

2) Place a tin can filled with paraffin or old candles in a pot of boiling water. Melting wax is very flammable, so you must watch it constantly.

3) For some holiday color, dye the wax with red candles or red crayons.

4) Pour the melted wax into oiled muffin tins, about a third to half full. Cut a piece of cotton candle wick about three inches long and place this on the wax after the wax has hardened slightly.

5) Place the pine cone on top of the wick and wax. Allow the wax to completely dry and harden, then remove them from the muffin tins. Voila! To kindle a fire, simply place one of these fire starters in the wood stove or fireplace and light the wick.

❧ Design **Holiday cards or Stationery** from evergreen leaf rubbings. Place the greens beneath thick white paper and rub them with the side of a crayon. Watch as a beautiful relief print emerges!

STARTING A NURSERY FOR BABY TREES

John Burroughs said: "When you plant a tree with love, it always lives, you do it with such care and thoroughness." Begin a nursery by planting orange seeds, plum or peach seeds, avocado pits, pine cone seeds and acorns.

🐚 **Avocados** are friendly because they are easier to grow than most other pits. Poke three or four toothpicks into the pit, about 1/3 of the way up from the bottom. Suspend the pit over a jar of water, making sure the water level reaches the toothpicks. Don't allow the water to evaporate below that level or the avocado pit might dry out and not germinate. After the tap root comes down and finer roots follow, it's time for a home in a pot of soil. Avocados can grow quite fast and are rewarding tree friends. Try one!

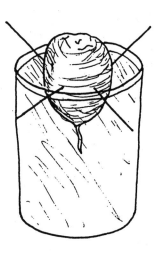

🐚 **Citrus seeds** will also grow well if you are careful not to let them dry out. After eating the fruit, rinse the seeds and plant them in a 6" pot of well-moistened soil. To keep the soil damp, set up a nursery greenhouse. Spread a plastic bag over the top of the nursery, and secure the plastic to the box with a rubber band. As the seedling emerges, give it room to grow by making a frame for the plastic. Take two short lengths of flexible wire and bend them into U-shapes. Put the ends down into the soil. Place the plastic over this frame - and watch! The plastic will help keep the growing seedling moist. Grow seed, grow!

❧ **Fruit pits** such as plum or peach pits, should be cleaned to remove clinging fruit and juices. Otherwise, the seed will ferment rather than germinate. Try a couple of different kinds of fruit pits. It's not easy to grow a baby tree if its parents are not around to give advice.

Squirrels And You: Tree Planters Two

❧ Be a squirrel next time you're outdoors and look for a Winter **acorn** cache. Look on the forest floor. Do you see a small area that looks as if it was scratched open? What do you think this scratched area might be? Often this is a sign that squirrels have been digging for their buried stash of acorns. They can locate each acorn by scent. What do you think might happen to some of the foraged acorns which are not recovered by the squirrels? You may find young acorns germinating in the soil, or even young oak seedlings from the year before.

Gather an acorn or two while hiking. Bring these acorns inside to germinate your own tree nursery. The acorns have already had their cool Winter's rest beneath the blanket of snow, and are now ready to set out roots. Bring some inside, make a wish for luck, and plant them in recycled paper cups filled with moist potting soil. Place some old leaves on top of the soil for a blanket so they will feel at home. Regularly rock the cradle and sing a lullaby to encourage them to germinate. Sh-h-h and have patience, never disturb a sleeping baby. It can be some time before these little ones wake up. Tend your tree nursery with the help of your parents, local elders, or the school maintenance crew.

(continued)

🍂 Can you locate **mature, brown pine cones** outdoors that are starting to open? Bring them indoors and place them in a slow oven, about 200°, until the pine cone opens fully. Take out the seeds that are hidden near the core of the pine cone. Plant the pine seeds in soil. It will take a month for them to germinate.

🍂 What do baby trees need? Make a **list** of all the things Mother Nature provides for trees to grow. Follow her good example when caring for your tree nursery.

Want To Do More?

🍂 **Contact your local tree nursery or forest service** for advice about other types of tree seeds that can grow in your area. Start a tree nursery of **seedlings for sale** on Spring Arbor Day or on Earth Day, April 22.

🍂 You may enjoy hearing the story of **<u>The Man Who Planted Trees</u>**, written by Jean Gioni. Elzeard Bouffier was a solitary shepherd who devoted his life to planting one hundred acorns a day for thirty years. As a result of his tireless task, he reforested a large part of France that had been barren. After listening to this heart-warming story, act out a skit or retell the story in your own words.

WHAT DO WE PLANT WHEN WE PLANT A TREE?

What do we plant when we plant a tree? Discover which trees are used in products around your home, school or neighborhood.

    ❧ **Different trees offer different qualities and gifts.** Some trees are good for the construction of cabins and homes, while others provide lumber for transportation vehicles - such as ships, canoes, and wagons. Some trees are used to construct articles for play - such as sleds, stilts, and tree houses. Some trees are consumed as food, or used as utensils for eating food. Some tree products have medicinal value. Most trees provide beauty and a place to call home.

What would your environment be like if you removed every object made from trees from your home or classroom?

    ❧ The following poem is wonderful for choral speaking. Or create a book that illustrates the words.

"What Do We Plant When We Plant A Tree?"

"What do we plant when we plant the tree?
We plant the ship which will cross the sea,
We plant the the mast to carry the sails,
We plant the planks to withstand the gales -
The keel, the keelson, the beam and knee -
We plant the ship when we plant the tree.

What do we plant when we plant the tree?
We plant the houses for you and me,
We plant the rafters, the shingles, the floors,

We plant the studding, the lath, the doors,
The beams and siding, all parts that be,
We plant the house when we plant the tree.

What do we plant when we plant the tree?
A thousand things that we daily see.

by Henry Abbey

FORCING BUDS AND BLOSSOMS INDOORS

Get a head start on Mother Spring by forcing buds indoors. Budding blossoms and unfurling leaves certainly perk up the end of a dreary winter!

🍂 Branches that look bare and plain are full of beauty and blossoms just waiting to come in out of the cold and burst forth in a warm room. Put on your hat and mittens and collect some of these hidden beauties!

(continued)

You will need:

sharp knife or pruning shears
variety of trees and shrubs
vase
water

1) In March, search for buds on your favorite trees or shrubs. With a sharp knife or pruning shears, cut a 12- to 18-inch branch from a maple, apple, cherry, forsythia, pussy willow or hobble bush. Do not cut more than a couple of branches from a single tree. Cut branches on a day when the temperature is above freezing.

2) Place the branches in a vase of water in a sunny window.

3) Observe the branches for several days, even weeks, to see what happens inside those bud cases. Keep the water fresh by changing it regularly.

4) Record your discoveries about changing buds in your tree journals.

♠ *Give a vase of buds to a neighbor who can't roam the winter forest as you can. Bring the forest home to them!*

♠ *Plan the timing for a special Buds and Blossom Fundraiser around Spring Equinox, March 21! You can make vases by decorating recycled half gallon juice cans, milk cartons or glass jars. With the money you earn, purchase a tree to green up your school grounds, neighborhood or back yard.*

THE FRIENDS OF THE FOREST WINTER TREE TRAIL

Students of nature have much to share! A Friends of the Forest Tree Trail can be established at your school, neighborhood, or in an adjacent forest. Not only is making the trail fun, but once it is made you can display your winter forest knowledge by hosting guided tours!

 First, determine the path of the Tree Trail and the trees that will be included in the walking path. You can simply drag your feet through the snow to mark a trail. Or, if you like, you can mark the trail by hanging colorful cloth strips or surveyor's tape along the trail's path. You can also create wooden signs or fabric banners to identify trees and points of interest. You'll probably pass your EARS station along the way!

 Choose any of the following activities for the Tree Trail Tours, or create your own ideas. You might find it helpful to have a trial run of these activities before inviting your neighbors to join the fun!

1) Do the **Hug A Tree** exercises recommended in "Old Man Wintree", page 123.

2) Make up **tree rhymes** or clues to **remember different species**. For example:

   ♠ For **White Pine** Trees, five needles in a cluster spells W-H-I-T-E. Red Pines have two needles per cluster.

   ♠ For **Staghorn Sumac**, look for the velvet-covered branch that resembles the antler of the stag

   ♠ For **Beech Tree**, look for a trunk that resembles an elephant's leg and twigs that have sharp, pointy yellow buds. Sometimes you will find triangular, bristly nut cases. When

these open, golden nuts drop out. Squirrels love them, and
so do bears!

♠ Some trees have **opposite leaf arrangements** that help in
their identification. Remember: **"Mad Horse"** means
Maple, **A**sh, **D**ogwood and **Horse** Chestnut.

3) **Bark rubbings** along the trail help visitors identify tree bark textures.
Wear your backpacks during the Tree Trail Tour, have some crayons
handy and bring some easel paper. For group rubbings, fasten a large
sheet of easel paper around the tree. Rub the easel paper with the
side of a crayon. What do you see? Use new easel paper along the
Tree Trail whenever the old sheet becomes full. Save the bark rubbings and piece them together later as a giant tree rubbing banner -
and add some tree-safe graffiti!

4) Make **bud identification cards** to identify tree species on the Tree
Trail. Simply laminate illustrations and add yarn loops so that the
cards can be worn around your neck during your Friends of the Forest
Tree Trail Tour.

5) Before your tour, choose two trees on the trail. **Draw and record
details** of special characteristics of these two trees, such as insect
and animal homes, branch patterns, bark textures, or mosses. What is
similar or different about these trees? Choose several of these no-
table characteristics and point them out to the group when leading a
Tree Trail Tour!

🐾 Prepare to lead **Tree Trail Tours** for family members, classmates
and friends of the neighborhood! Advertise an official Opening Day of the
Friends of the Forest Tree Trail, and invite people to come on Tree Trail
Tours.

FRIENDS OF THE FOREST WINTER FESTIVAL

Culminate the Winter activities by sharing and celebrating your discoveries in a community event.

🍂 Create an **Indoor Forest** for friends of the forest to explore. Use tree thinnings or create your own cardboard trees. Have your guests search for hidden objects as they wander through the indoor forest. Objects can include a snake skin, shelf fungus, crystal, snail shell, fox tracks, a nest, and so on. These hidden objects should not be touched or removed.

🍂 Display your larger-than-life **rotting tree diorama.** Let your friends of the forest peek at the hidden mysteries you've concealed beneath the bark.

🍂 Display your **rotting log terrarium.** Demonstrate how to make a rotting log terrarium from a recycled jar with lid. Have extra recycled jars with lids on hand, with photocopied instructions, so that your guests can make their own terrariums at home.

🍂 **Invite Old Man Wintree** to come in costume and answer questions about trees in the Wintertime. Old Man Wintree can wear a bark mask or any other creative outfit you can imagine. Old Man Wintree would make a wonderful Master of Ceremonies!

🍂 Make a **"smells of the forest" booth** to challenge your guests. See if they can identify the contents of sniffy jars and feely bags filled with mysterious forest objects.

🍂 Since you will be hosting the Festival, wouldn't it be nice to dress up as **Friends of the Forest**? You can wear the Friends of the Forest **T-shirts** you have designed. Add some **tree costume** details. Wear green and brown pants or vests, and fasten cedar branches around your waist.

(continued)

Robin Hood hats can be made from folded newspaper that has been painted green, or it can be sewn from green felt. Simple green capes with felt forest leaf applique are fun to make - wear or sell them. Or **dress up as friends of the forest characters**, such as owl, fox, rabbit, woodpecker, snail, deer, mushroom, fern, salamander, toad, moth, ovenbird, chipmunk, squirrel, robin, butterfly, mosquito. As hosts, each of you should have an assignment or activity for the day.

Want To Do More?

You have a lot to share about trees during this festive community event. Here are some activities that will help you celebrate this busy day.

🐾 Put on a skit about trees, such as "The Lorax" or "The Man Who Planted Trees". Or recite Chief Seattle's Address, found in Fall's "A Family Under One Sky: Webs of Life", page 118.

🐾 Lead Tree Trail Tours.

🐾 Make tree art, such as leaf rubbing stationery, tree branch weavings, or nature blocks. Share any tree art you can think of!

🐾 Costumed Friends of the Forest characters can play a **Hibernation Memory Game** with festival guests:

All the forest characters stand in a circle inside a circle of guests. Allow the guests time to examine each character, then have them close their eyes. While the guests' eyes are closed, some of the hibernating forest characters leave the inner circle and camouflage or hide themselves. When the guests open their eyes, they try to recall which characters are missing.

🐾 Play the **Tree Shape game,** a fun event in which participants mimic **tree silhouettes** of some common trees, described on the following page:

The Tree Shape Game

♠ To play, form a circle with ample room between neighbors so that each can create the shape of a tree with her body. Invite a guests to stand in the center with her eyes closed. Have her spin, pointing her arm toward the circle of players, who spin about chanting:

> Some are green, some are gray
> All their leaves have slipped away.
> Triangle and ball,
> Umbrella or fan,
> Tree shapes -
> brighten up the land.
> Can you guess, do you know
> The name of the tree that I now show?

When the chant is finished, the players freeze in a tree silhouette of their choice. The spinner opens her eyes and tries to guess the name of the tree she is pointing to. If she guesses correctly, one of the tree imitators becomes the spinner.

• When playing the tree shape game, it is best to begin with the shapes of trees that live in your area. Feel free to add other tree species and adapt the chant to include them.

♠ Here are some **suggested tree shapes** to act out:

• **Conifers** are triangular-shaped - stand with your legs apart, arms at sides, to mimic a triangle

• **Maples** tend to be round - arms over head, hands touching to create a circle.

• **Elms** are fan-shaped - stand with arms overhead, arching out like a fan.

• **Weeping Willows** have sheltering boughs - stand with arms dangling downward, creating a protective, umbrella-shaped shelter.

(continued)

• **Poplars** and some old tree trunks reach straight up - reach arms together straight overhead.

🐦 Festival guests can create **Friends of the Forest banners** by painting on large pieces of cloth or large easel paper. When the banners are dry, display them on the walls.

🐦 Be sure to **serve tree foods** at the festival. Try maple products, nuts, fruit salads, guacamole dips, coconut milk and meat, and almond butter - fresh ground, of course.

🐦 To close the Festival, **Teach "My Roots Go Down"** to festival guests, who should stand in a large circle around the conductor, Old Man Wintree.

🐦 It helps to **organize** your **Friends of the Forest Winter Festival** by separating the day into its different parts:

    1) Opening Circle:
        • "My Roots Go Down"

    2) Scheduled Demonstrations:
        • Tree Trail Tours
        • The Rotting Log Terrarium

    3) Scheduled or Ongoing Theater:
        • Skits
        • Friends of the Forest Costumes
        • Old Man Wintree

    4) Ongoing Activities:
        • Indoor Forest
        • Rotting Tree Diorama
        • Smells of the Forest

- Tree Art
- Forest Banners
- Tree Foods

5) Scheduled Games:
- Tree Shapes
- Hibernation Hide 'N Seek

6) Closing Circle:
- "My Roots Go Down"

HAPPY WINTER!

Spring

GRANDFOREST TREE TELLS A STORY

If the trees could whisper stories and tell you their secrets, what might they say? Listen to the words of Grandforest Tree. . .

"The Evergreens Tell of the Promise of Spring"

In the unpredictable days of yore, Winter Warriors ruled the land for six months of the year. Each Fall, Warrior Frost painted the leaves of trees, who longed to keep their beautiful foliage forever. Then Warrior Storm Wind would command that every tree drop its leaves, for he wanted to destroy the power that Spring had given them. If the trees did not cooperate, Warrior Storm Wind pulled every leaf from the trees with his fierce, gusty gales. Warrior Winter roared with delight at the sight of the leafless trees. He was glad to rob the Sun of her friends, and relished the fact that all signs of Spring had been banished.

"In those forgotten days, the trees had tongues and could speak. The Chief of the needle-leaf trees, White Pine, saw what was happening. He called a council of the Evergreens and asked: 'Who will stand with me as Winter comes, to show he will always be a friend to the Sun and to Spring?'

'I will,' said the Red Pine.
'I will,' said the Cedar.
'I will,' said the Hemlock.
'I will,' said the Spruce.
'I will,' said the Balsam.

"'Where is Tamarack?' asked White Pine, who had not heard Tamarack's voice. Tamarack had arrived late for the council

meeting, bringing Oak with him. Now he rose up so White Pine could see him. 'Do you stand with us, Tamarack?' asked White Pine. 'Will you defy Winter?'

"'Yes, I will defy Winter,' said Tamarack. 'Now Oak, who is not of our tribe, wishes to speak.'

"Oak said, 'I am a friend of the Sun, though I am not of your tribe. My leaves are broad, but I shall hold them and rattle them in Winter's face when he laughs at the other bare trees.'

"White Pine commended Oak's brave challenge of the Warriors, adding: 'It is so, then. We will drink a magic oil that will keep us green and strong, able to defy the strongest of the Winter Warriors.'

"Tamarack, who was an ornery fellow, did not want to believe that Oak could endure Winter Storm Wind. He was also jealous of White Pine's admiration of Oak. After the council adjourned, Tamarack jeered at Oak, saying that Oak would never be able to retain his leaves. But Oak remained steadfast: 'I will hold my leaves, no matter what comes.'

"Once again Autumn began with Warrior Frost's brilliant painting of the leaves. He turned Maple leaves red, orange and yellow, Birch and Aspen leaves yellow, and Oak's leaves scarlet. However, the Evergreen tribe trees refused to change their colors. And when Warrior Storm Wind tried to remove the Evergreen's leaves, hardly a needle was lost. Tamarack, however, steeped in jealousy, had forgotten to drink the magic oil that kept his tribe green and strong. His needles turned a brilliant gold for all the world, and himself, to admire.

"One day, as Tamarack was strutting about and showing off his golden coat, Warrior Storm Wind blew fiercely. In an instant all of Tamarack's gorgeous golden needles were swept away! What a sorry sight!

"For many moons, Warrior Frost, Warrior Winter and Warrior Storm Wind continued to unleash their fury. But after the moon had grown full fivetimes, Sister Spring finally managed to drive the Winter Warriors away. All of the Evergreens, save Tamarack, stood proudly with Oak on the hill. Each was clothed in his green robes to show he was a friend of the Sun.

"Tamarack, however, stood alone in the swampy lowlands, where you can still see him to this day. Though Tamarack's leaves grow again every Spring, he loses them each year after Warrior Frost's Autumn visit."

♠ Can you act out or retell this Native tale?

♠ Can you find the friends of the Sun: a White Pine, Red Pine, Cedar, Oak, Tamarack, Spruce and Balsam tree?

"The Secret of Tree-Water"

With the coming of Spring, the sap begins to rise up into the trees. Even before the first birdsong can be heard, the Maple tree brings us its delicious sweet syrup. When the days are warm, but the nights still freeze, you will hear the "plink, plink, plink" of sap flowing into the sap buckets. There are many stories about how we discovered the secret of the Sugar Maple, but Grandforest Tree loves most the story his grandfather told him.

It is said that Native Americans discovered the wonderful sweetness of maple sap, but we trees know better. While it is true they were the first to boil the sap to make syrup, Squirrel was the original harbinger of spring's sweet gift. Let me tell you the story my grandfather told me, about how the knowledge of Maple sap and syrup-making came to humans.

"One late-winter morning, Child-Who-Watches sat contentedly on a log while her father hunted Grouse. She loved the coming of spring, when it was warm enough to be still for hours in the deep woods, watching the comings and goings of animals.

"The day was sunny and windless, warm enough to make snowballs or snow forts. The March sky was a rich purple-blue. Chickadees flitted about singing their spring song. Several different kinds of tracks crisscrossed the soft snowy woods, proof that many animals had awakened from their winter naps. Child-Who-Watches closed her eyes for a few moments and listened to the pulse of spring. Fluttering wings, chirps, flashes of song, rat-a-tat-tappings and busy scurrying sounds filled the air. Playing bass in the background was the soft fussssh of trickling water.

"When she opened her eyes she noticed that Squirrel was investigating a wet splotch on the trunk of a nearby Maple tree. The splotch was caused by water dripping from a broken branch high in the tree. Child-Who-Watches looked on as Squirrel's little pink tongue lapped the wet bark. The furry little animal was so intent on her task that she did not notice Child-Who-Watches' pink tongue lapped the wet bark. The furry little animal was so intent on her task that she did not notice Child-Who-Watches' father, Star Fire, approaching.

"'Look, Father,' said Child-Who-Watches. 'Watch how Squirrel licks the trunk of that Maple tree. Maybe he is trying to tell us something!' By this time Squirrel, aware of potential danger, had scurried into the protective branches of an evergreen. Curious, Child-Who-Watches walked over to the Maple tree and tasted the wet bark. To her surprise, it tasted slightly sweet.

"'Father, taste the water that drips down the bark. See how sweet it is!' Star Fire stepped forward and tasted the rough wet trunk. He smiled in surprise. Squirrel certainly did know something!

"'Yes, the water is sweet. Plenty for squirrel to drink, but not enough for us. We can fetch water from the melting snows and streams. Come, let us move on. I found some rabbit tracks. Would you like rabbit stew for dinner?'

"'Oh, yes!' Child-Who-Watches replied. She started to follow her father, then took a step back towards the tree. With her knife she cut several slits in its trunk. '"There, Squirrel, now you will have plenty to drink!' And off she waddled on her snow-shoes through the brilliant late-winter day.

"The next day, Child-Who-Watches joined her father again as he hunted. This time she sat on a deerskin at the edge of a still-frozen pond. As she glanced around, she noticed several tree limbs that had been torn off during winter storms. Upon closer inspection she saw that some of them were from Maple trees. She wandered closer. Sure enough, water dripped steadily from the severed branches, making yellow stains on the soft snow. Child-Who-Watches placed a birch basket beneath one of the trees to collect the dripping water.

"Soon after the sun began its descent into the southwestern sky, Child-Who-Watches checked the water in the basket. Already there was plenty to drink with her noonday meal. By the end of the day there would be enough to take home for the evening meal. Child-Who-Watches decided to keep the tree water a secret

from her father. This evening she would surprise her family with a delicious drink!

"Soon Star Fire came back with the carcass of a deer. Child-Who-Watches helped her father build a make-shift sled so it would be easier to carry the deer. By the time they finished, the sun was one hand above the ridge. The air had cooled and the tree branch no longer dripped. As her father pulled the sled, heading for home, Child-Who-Watches carefully poured the collected water into a waterproof pouch made from a bear's stomach. Then she followed her Father.

"That evening Child-Who-Watches looked on with pleasure as her family drank the fresh tree-water, everyone exclaiming at its delicious taste. 'It is a gift from Squirrel,' explained Child-Who-Watches. She described the furry animal's antics on the Maple tree.

"'Child-Who-Watches, you are well named!" Grandmother proclaimed. 'We must give thanks to Squirrel for this water. Surely it is sacred.'

"The next day, clouds covered the sun and snow began to fall. The storm lasted for several days. Though windless and relatively warm, the snow fell steadily. When at last the sun finally reappeared, several feet of the fluffy snow had accumulated.

"As soon as possible, Child-Who-Watches returned to the Maple Tree carrying a generous handful of nuts and seeds for Squirrel. She placed the offering on a nearby stump and waited for Squirrel to emerge. Soon the furry little creature appeared. Squirrel sniffed the air, then scampered over to the stump and sat down to enjoy her first meal in several days. She was very grateful, for all her food stores were buried beneath the heavy snow.

"Squirrel was halfway through her meal when suddenly she sniffed a human scent. She stopped eating and looked directly at Child-Who-Watches. Time seemed to stand still as a look of understanding passed between the little animal and the young girl. Despite the cool March air, Child-Who-Watches felt warmed with the glow of friendship.

When Squirrel had had her fill, she began carrying the remains of her meal back to her nest. Child-Who-Watches placed some more nuts on the stump, then snowshoed back to camp.

"That night Child-Who-Watches had a strange dream. In it, squirrels ran about like people, tending fires, gathering wood and water and celebrating. Many of them excitedly gathered the tree water and poured it into cooking baskets. In the dream, Child-Who-Watches walked over to a cooking pot and looked in. A thick, brown syrupy substance bubbled and frothed, giving off the most delicious smell! One of the squirrels handed her a small piece of hardened brown candy, indicating it came from one of the cooking pots. Child-Who-Watches put the candy in her mouth, and tasted its wonderful sweetness.

"When she awoke, the taste of maple lingered on her lips. She went to Grandmother with her dream. Grandmother knew instantly that it was a message. 'We should do as the squirrels did in the dream,' she said. 'Gather the sap - the sweet water - from the trees and boil it down to make sugar.'

"From that year forth, the people in Child-Who-Watches' village collected the sap each spring. Often they would use it for cooking. Or they would boil it down into sugar, which kept for a long time.

"And, just as my grandfather told it to me, that is the story of Maple Syrup!

MAPLE TREE: ANNOUNCER OF SPRING

As the sap in the Maple tree starts to run in New England, the sweet flow of life returns to the land. The Native people honor this time of year by celebrating the "Maple Moon" or "Sugar Moon". When the sap begins to run slow, watch the Earth awaken from its long winter sleep. What natural events announce Spring where you live?

❧ Maple Magic: Disappearing Liquids

Grandmother placed the Maple sap on the cooking fire and let it boil for a long time before it turned to thick brown syrup. What happened to all the water in the sap? Did it simply disappear? You can discover how liquids seem to disappear by doing a simple experiment. Boil a cup of water in a pot. After five or ten minutes, measure the water that remains in the pot. How much is there? Where is the rest of the water? Can you explain what happened? The water e-"vapor"-ated.

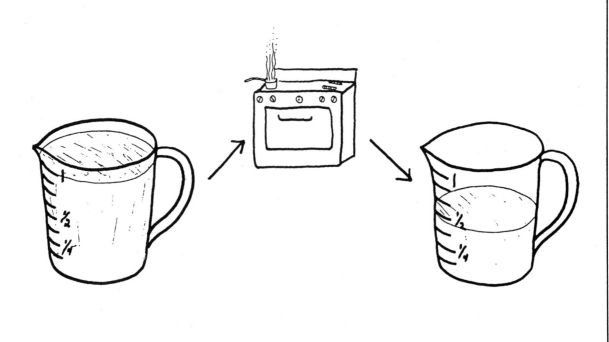

🐝 Apple Sap to Apple Syrup

Now make some Apple juice using frozen Apple juice concentrate. Follow the directions on the Apple juice container and mix the concentrate with the proper amount of water. Taste the juice before continuing your experiment.

With the supervision of an adult, measure one cup of Apple juice and boil it on the stove top. Do you see bubbles forming in the juice as it cooks? What are the bubbles doing? Do you see a cloud forming above the cooking pot? This cloud is made of **water vapor**. As the water droplets e-"vapor"-ate into the air, the cloud disappears. Though the cloud can no longer be seen, the evaporated vapor is still present in the air. Now it is simply one of many invisible gases that make up our sky.

Continue cooking the Apple juice until it becomes dark and thick. What happened to the watery part of the juice? Did it evaporate? Taste what remains in the pot. Is it thicker and sweeter now that all the water has evaporated from the juice? What you have left is Apple syrup. Maple sap works in much the same way as the Apple juice. The water evaporates from the sap, leaving a fine, thick sweet syrup.

Want To Do More?

Child-Who-Watches discovered how to make Maple syrup a long time ago and, thankfully, Maple farmers still harvest Maple sap and boil it down to make syrup today. Visit a Maple sugar bush near you to enjoy these late winter and early spring festivities. If you're lucky, you might catch the farmer boiling down the sap!

(continued)

🐝 Maple Magic Math

The ratio of sap to syrup is 40 to 1. That means it takes 40 gallons of sap to make 1 gallon of syrup. Try the following demonstration to get a sense of how much water is needed to produce 1 cup of syrup. Pour 40 cups of water into some gallon jugs. (40 cups equals 2 and 1/2 gallons.) Now fill a cup of water. Pretend the water in the cup is Maple syrup. Compare the single cup of liquid to the 40 cups of water in the gallon jugs. Quite a difference!

Alternatively, fill 41 separate cups with water. Place 40 of the cups in a row on a table, and compare them to the single cup of water.

🐝 Mmmmmaple Magic Recipes

Bake and compare the following recipes, sweetening them with Maple syrup or Apple juice concentrate.

Maple Bread Pudding

2 Tbs. butter
3/4 cup Maple syrup or Apple juice concentrate
2 beaten eggs
1 cup milk
4 slices bread torn in cubes

Melt butter, add Maple syrup or Apple juice concentrate. Add this to beaten eggs, milk and bread cubes. Simmer one hour and serve with whipped cream.   Makes 4 servings.

Maple Oatmeal Cookies

1 cup flour   1/2 cup oil
1/4 tsp. salt   1 egg
1 tsp. baking powder   3/4 cup Maple syrup
1 cup uncooked oats   1/2 tsp. vanilla
1/2 cup chopped walnuts

    Mix dry ingredients. Cream oil, egg, syrup, and vanilla until light. Mix wet and dry ingredients together. Drop by spoonful onto greased cookie sheet. Bake at 400 for 8-12 minutes. Makes 3 dozen cookies.

Even More Curious?

    Read other stories about the first Maple tree or the origins of Maple sap, such as Bruchac's "Gluskabe and the Maple Trees" in <u>Faithful Hunter</u>. Retell these stories or write your own story about the first Maple syrup. These stories will be fun to tell whenever you enjoy Maple syrup!

SPRING EQUINOX: MAPLE THANKSGIVING FESTIVAL

O, Forest!
We give thanks for your sweet water.
We are grateful for the promise of Spring,
For the sweetness the Earth brings forth.
O, Forest!
We give thanks for a place of peace and beauty,
For all our children. Ho!"

Celebrate the gifts of the Maple tree and the Spring Equinox! In New England, Maple sugaring season heralds the beginning of Spring. It begins in March and usually runs through Spring Equinox, when buds appear on the trees. The middle of the season is generally around St. Patrick's Day. Celebrate a Maple Thanksgiving Spring Equinox Festival by sharing your discoveries of this wonderful time of year with your family, class, school or community.

Some ideas to get you started:

❧ Prepare and present a **skit** about Child-Who-Watches, or read and act out "Manabozho and the Maple Trees" from Michael Caduto's <u>Keepers of the Earth.</u>

❧ **Collect your own sap** and evaporate it to form Maple syrup. Ask a local sugar maker to help you with this project.

❧ Serve **Maple snacks**. "Snowfood" is popcorn and hot maple syrup. Sometimes the Iroquois ate it for breakfast cereal! "Sugar on Snow" is another Native food treat. Simply place a handful of snow in a bowl and pour Maple syrup over it. Mmm, delicious!

❧ Serve **traditional** and **Native American maple recipes** at a community meal. Try maple sugar and syrup as a seasoning in cornbread,

pumpkin pie or bean dishes. Invite local elders, neighbors, sugar makers, and Native Americans from your community, and - if you celebrate the Maple Thanksgiving Festival at your school - even the kitchen crew!

🍃 As the Iroquois people say: "O? tahinonyo? neh wahda? We give thanks to the Maple." Plan a Festival for expressing the ways in which you are thankful for having Maple trees and for having survived the starving months of Winter. Invite the community to **share your thanks** by joining hands in a circle around a real or imagined Maple tree. Let each person speak her thanks for a particular Maple tree gift. This ceremony can also include music, drumming or dance.

🍃 Plan a future date for **planting Maple trees** around your home, school or community. This might coincide with Arbor Day in late April.

SONGS OF SPRING HIKE

When the Earth is beginning to wake from its dreamy winter sleep, go on a spring hike! Look, listen, smell and sense the magic of new life.

🌰 Listen for the **spring chorus** sung by the forest dwellers! Whenever you hear animal chatter, stop walking. Close your eyes and listen. Clench your hand into a fist and put it on top of your head. Each time you hear a sound, put up one finger. Do this for a minute or so, then check to see how many fingers you have put up.

🌰 If you are with a group of friends, have them do the same thing. After a minute, everyone can open her eyes and look at her friends to see how many fingers are up. Does everyone look as if she is wearing a feather headdress? Can you understand what the songs are saying? What other voices did you hear? What else did you notice? Try to **echo some of the songs** you heard.

Here are some **Sun Songs of Spring** you might hear:

"Okalee-e-e-e", call of the redwing blackbird.
"Fee-bee", spring song of the chickadee.
"Honking" of the returning goose or duck flock.
"Buzz-zzing" of bees.
"Teacher, teacher, teacher", sung by the ovenbird.
"Ping, ping, ping", the sap buckets ring.

Some Moon Songs of Spring to listen for:

"Peep, peep, peep, peep" of the peeper night chorus.
"Who-who-who-whooooo" or "Who cooks for you, who cooks for you all?" asks the owl calling for a mate.

"Peent, peent, peent" (nasal sounding), the woodcock sings.
"Ker-splash", the beaver's tail sends a warning.

❧ **Play "Frog Call", a fun nature game, day or night.**

To play, everyone teams up with a partner frog. Each set of partners agrees on a particular "frog call" it will sing when searching for its partner. When all the frogs are ready, they begin to mingle with the other frogs in the pond. At a given signal, such as an owl call, the frogs hop for safety. All close their eyes. Now each frog sings out his frog call, and with his eyes still closed, searches for his partner. The game ends when all sets of partners are safely reunited.

❧ In a **Share Circle**, create your own **"Songs of Spring Chorus"**. You can accompany the chorus with musical instruments made from nature objects, such as tree xylophones, rhythm sticks, or drumming logs.

Crrroak!

Guided Journey

THE WISE ELDER TREE WALK

Stop by a stand of old dying trees and look for signs of Spring in the old trees. If you don't see any signs of Spring, do you think it means there's no life here?

Find an old dead tree that you especially like, and hug it as you listen to this Guided Journey....

What have these ancient ones, Grandfather and Grand mother Tree, seen over time? What stories could these Wise Elders tell? Close your eyes and, searching with your fingertips around and up and down the trunk, explore Grandfather or Grandmother Tree. Search for ant holes, woodpecker holes, branches, moss, shelf fungus. . . . Feel all the way up and all the way down to its roots. . . . Find all the ways Grandmother or Grandfather Tree shares life with others. . . . When you are finished, open your eyes, step away and look at the shape of Grandfather or Grandmother Tree. Does this tree have a story to tell you? Listen. . . . Now shape your body into the shape of your wise tree friend and silently, in return for all which was given, tell Grandmother or Grandfather Tree the story told to you."

🐝 You can make a **Circle of Life** drawing showing all the ways an old tree shares its life with others, such as ants, beetles, lichen, moss, fungus, snails, woodpeckers, and hawks. Don't forget to include decomposing limbs creating soil for those who follow, or wildflowers growing in the shelter of the tree.

✍ *Sitting beside the wise elder tree, record your ideas in your journal by using illustrations. Can you draw the tree branches at the top of the crown of the tree, or the bottom branches, to look as if they were giving something away? What gift of life can you draw on each branch?*

With a group of friends you can **paint a mural**, called "Old Life Givers", to illustrate all the ways trees do this important work of giving away life to others.

HAPPY BIRTHDAY TO WILDFLOWERS WALK

Have you ever been invited to a Wildflower's birthday party? You're invited *today!*

During a woodlands wildflower hike, stop and sit beside a newly emerging plant. Today might be its birthday, for a new plant springs up each year! Touch it gently. Smell it. Study all the amazing details of this forest gem. Look at all its wonders - stem, leaves, petals, color, smell, shape.

🌿 As you sit beside your favorite wildflower, observe, feel and smell its **special qualities**. You might see a downy coat along its stem. Mother Nature provides this coat to protect the wildflower from the early Spring chill. You might notice large leaves. These create food when they soak up sunbeams and drink water. Can you find a blossom, sweetly-scented and colorful? The flower hopes to attract a bee. Sometimes, however, a flower will have an unpleasant odor to repel hungry deer or rabbits.

🌿 Look for **patterns** in your flower's design.

- Is your flower symmetrical or asymmetrical?
- How many petals does your flower friend have? Is this an odd or even number?
- How many sepals do you count?
- Is the number of sepals less than, more than, or equal to the number of petals?

> ☛ *Note:* Some flowers, called composites, are actually flowers within flowers. Dandelion is an example. The yellow "petals" in a dandelion are actually separate flowers. Take note of this when you count the petals!

🌿 Think about your plant's special qualities. Choose a **name** that you feel describes it. Build a little shelter or **fairy house** around your flower friend, using fallen materials like twigs, leaves, or scraps of birch bark. Designate it as a protected place. When you are finished, invite a friend on a guided tour. Point out the lessons the plant has shared with you, as well as the little house where the fairy lives.

🌿 Did you know that the flower of a trout lily takes seven years to form? If you found a blooming trout lily, how old would it be? Add up all the trout lily blossoms by adding in sevens to determine how many candles you need for today's woodland birthday cake.

🌿 Before you leave, don't forget to **sing Happy Birthday** to your beautiful blossoming wildflower!

(continued)

Want To Do More?

🐛 Mimic the emergence of a wildflower and recreate some of its qualities in the following **guided movement exercise.**

"Curled up tightly within the care of Mother Earth, a sturdy root dreamed of the arrival of Spring. One day as the root was sleeping, soft, cool water began to bathe it, waking it from its dreamy Winter state. Then sunbeams visited, their warmth reaching deep into the dark, moist earth. The sunbeams called to the root, encouraging its stem to reach up - up - upward toward the sun's warm glow.

"Slowly, with a great stretching and reaching, the plant began to rise from the darkness of Winter's rest. It unfolded slowly, reaching, seeking, remembering the sky and sun. Then the leaves burst forth, gathering sunbeams and drawing them inside. Nourished by earth and sky, the flower buds bowed their heads in waiting. Finally a blossom opened its face to the sun, filling the air with its fragrant scent, announcing its arrival to all the forest and all the sky. "I am here, see me shine!"

🐛 Food works for flowers in the Forest! How does this happen? You can demonstrate this idea by making a **Wheel of Life.** Gather in a circle with some friends. Stand quietly for a minute or two, and think about what a wildflower needs. When you are ready, raise your hand and describe one of the wildflower's needs. Then reach your arm into the center of the circle, as though it were the spoke of a wagon wheel. Continue until everyone joins hands and the wheel takes form. When the wheel of life is complete, rotate the wheel by walking sunwise.

What happens if some of the wildflower's needs, such as soil, sunshine or bees, disappear? Choose two or three spokes to represent these life-giving elements. They should stand in place, instead of moving with the other spokes when the wheel rotates. What happens when the

wheel tries to move? Probably you will find that the broken spokes will not allow the the wheel to rotate. Is it a wheel of life now?

Try some Math, Nature's Way

🐦 **Take an inventory** of different kinds of plants growing in a specific area. First, measure a square or rectangular area that is large enough to include at least one tree. Record the perimeter that surrounds this space. Then estimate how many different kinds of plants are growing in that area. Count the actual number of different plants you see. Was your estimate less than or more than the number you counted?

Even More Curious?

🐦 Find out what's **blooming in the meadow-thicket!** Make a list (or a collection of drawings) of the flowers in the meadow-thicket, and another of the flowers found in the forest. Compare the two lists. Did you find the same flowers in the meadow-thicket as you did in the forest? Why do you think the forest is filled with flowers now, but not in midsummer when the meadow-thicket is all a-bloom? Why do meadow-thicket flowers bloom later?

GRANDFOREST TREE TELLS A STORY

Grandforest Tree knows the ways of the woods, and if you listen, will tell the cautionary tale of the forest guardians.

"Leaflets Three: Let It Be"

As the Earth awakens, Mother Spring calls each of her plant children and gives everyone a gift. These gifts should help you recognize the plant children, and discover a wonderful lesson about walking gently through the forest home.

"The last snow had barely melted when music filled the spring forest. It was the voice of Mother Spring, calling her plant children to her. She sang first to Hepatica. 'Hepatica, I give you the gift of a woolly stem to warm you on the cool nights of Spring, and to remind the children to dress warmly as well, until all the frosty days have passed.'

"Mother Spring called to Coltsfoot next. 'Coltsfoot', she sang, 'I give you a golden yellow cap of light. It will shine near the forest edge, in the bright open meadows, to guide the children who come here. The golden light of your blossom will show hikers where you dwell, for your leaves shall remain hidden from view until Summer is nearly here. In Autumn, when hikers return to enjoy the rainbow canopy of the forest, there at the forest's edge they shall find you again. Your leaf shall be the footprint of a young colt, and your leaves may be gathered as a healing tea for winter colds.'

"'Violet,' she called, 'come forward so that I may give you a gift. These heart-shaped leaves shall remind everyone that you love to live beneath the peaceful forest trees and listen to the stories the leaves tell the wind. Your violet blossoms are tasty,

and may be picked and enjoyed by woodland visitors. But your heart-shaped leaves shall remind the visitors to leave most of the violets in their woodland home so that you can grow anew each Spring. These leaves will also be a reminder to the visitors to give heartfelt thanks for the gifts of nature.'

"Mother Spring sang to Trout Lily next. 'Trout Lily, until your seventh birthday you shall wear leaves that are as spotted as the trout of the neighboring streams. This will remind people that the stream and the forest are sisters. On your seventh birthday, I shall give you the gift of a yellow, bell-shaped blossom. With this bell you can ring out a birthday song, which shall be heard throughout the woodlands.'

"Then Mother Spring sang to her final plant child, the Guardian of the Forest. 'Your gift shall be a rambling vine, which shall enable you to climb even the highest tree. As Guardian of the Forest, you will greet all who visit these woodlands. Your shining leaflets three shall wave both a welcome and a warning to the visitors - asking them to step gently among the flowers, ferns and fairy houses. You shall remind them that the forest is home to the trees, flowers and animals who dwell here. All visitors are welcome to enjoy some the peacefulness of the forest - they may even take a little of it away with them, and return at any time. But your shining leaflets three will warn them to limit what they take, and to behave themselves while they are here.'

"One Spring day, Leaflets Three watched from the height of a great tree as some hikers came to the forest. He waved a welcome to all who came, but he did not like what happened once they arrived. A few hikers walked gently, but some picked too many wildflowers and others whacked the tree trunks and branches with sticks. With a heavy heart, he told Mother Spring what had happened.

"'Guardian of the Forest,' she said, 'I see that your leaflets three warning works only some of the time. Some visitors remember, but others forget to listen to your gentle warnings. So I shall give you yet another gift. Here is some itching oil. Those who thrash about and do not heed your gentle warning will think twice about their behavior after coming into contact with you. Perhaps they will stop stealing the quiet from the forest, and will walk gently again.'

"And so to this day when you visit the forest, you shall see the gifts Mother Spring has given her plant children. And you will meet the Guardian of the Forest, Leaflets Three, who still uses his gifts to warn people to walk gently when they visit the woodlands."

♠ **Look for Mother Spring's gifts** to her plant children on your next woodlands hike. You may discover plants not mentioned in the story. Look closely at these plants. Discover for yourself what gifts they've been given, and what teachings they have to share with you.

♠ **Mother Spring** won't mind if you pick one plant of each wildflower variety you discover on your hike. Place them in your plant press so that they may dry. Then you will have some permanent examples of the gifts Mother Spring gives to her plant children.

♠ **Poison Ivy awareness** can be a hiker's best friend. Learn to identify these vines and leaf formations so that you can teach others about the Guardian of the Forest. Remedies for Poison Ivy often grow close by.

*Look for the **Jewelweed** plant, which likes the wetter areas along a forest's edge. Use a coarse brown soap to wash skin that has been exposed to Poison Ivy. <u>After</u> washing, crush some Jewelweed leaves, which contain a healing sap. Rub the Jewelweed sap on the areas that have been exposed to Poison Ivy.*

THE LANGUAGE OF WOODLAND WILDFLOWERS: A SPRING WOODLAND WILDFLOWER WALK

You may discover that every flower and plant has its own language or expression. If you take some time to befriend a plant, many of its qualities - and often its name - will be revealed to you.

🐝 Before going on a **Spring Woodland Wildflower Walk,** think about some of the common wildflowers that grow in your area. For example, have you heard of Skunk Cabbage, Spring Beauty, Violet, Trout Lily, Dutchman's Breeches, Squirrel Corn, Pink Moccasin, or Jack-in-the-Pulpit? Choose one whose name strikes you as interesting. Imagine what you think the flower might look like, then draw it. Do the same with the others. Display each of your plant creations.

On your hike, be on the lookout for each of the woodland wildflowers you illustrated from your imagination. These specimens are early to late spring bloomers, so plan to take weekly or bimonthly wildflower hikes until you've had the pleasure of discovering all of them.

After discovering what the spring wildflowers in your imagination really look like, **sketch or paint** these living plants. Display these illustrations alongside the ones you created from your imagination - and compare!

🐝 Pretend you have just found a wildflower no one has ever seen before. Since you are the one to make this rare discovery, you have the honor of naming it. Create a model of the new wildflower so that you can show the world your remarkable discovery! Do this using your favorite medium: painting, drawing, pastels, sculpting with beeswax or plasticene, tissue paper collage, or anything else that pleases you. Be sure to place the name you have given the plant near your creation.

LET THEM BE

Should we pick or protect the gentle young wildflowers that emerge like a miracle in our Spring woodlands?

"Let Them Be"

In early spring,
between the time of snowmelt and
the unfurling of leaves,
a brief magic happens in the woods.
From earths' bare bones,
pushing through snow-flattened carpets of leaves,
emerge the first flowers.
These surprises
creep up southern slopes,
and dance in sunny, sheltered nooks.
Soon, you will find them
even in the coolest spots
where sunshine briefly passes.
Homes for fairies and elves,
nectar for bees
harbingers of warmth -
let them be.
Let them bask in
warming winds,
as the foothold of winter eases.
Let them be
nuzzled by hungry bees,
let the wee beings
sleep in their blossoms.
Let them stay rooted
in the cool soils
of the forest.

J.H.

🐦 What do you think this poet is trying to tell you? What would you like to tell others about caretaking the woodland wildflowers?

🐦 Why is it important to protect wildflowers?

- ♠ Flowers add a gentle beauty, color, perfume and wonder to our world.
- ♠ Flowers produce pollen and nectar, which feed pollinating insects.
- ♠ Pollinated flowers produce seeds for future generations of trees or wildflowers.
- ♠ Pollinated flowers produce fruits, which feed animals.
- ♠ Flowering Medicinal plants heal us.
- ♠ Decomposing flowers return their gifts to the Earth by adding soil to the forest.

(continued)

🕊️ On a hike, identify what you think is precious and deserves protection.

What can you do?

🍎 You and your friends can **write letters** to the local chapter of the U.S. Department of Forests to tell them about your adopted tree and EARS. You may want to inquire about posters of woodland wildflowers and trees, which are often offered free to schools and organizations. Also, ask for the list of protected woodland species in your area.

SPRING WOODLAND FLOWERS

Here in the Northeast, May is the month when woodland wildflowers and flowering trees bloom. Have you ever noticed how nearly every day a different flower opens to greet the Spring?

❧ **Take a hike on a sunny May day,** and you will practically see the sun beckoning blossoms to open! Every week, a different family of wildflowers or trees bloom, so you can enjoy wildflower hikes weekly, until the end of the month.

❧ While identifying forest flowers according to characteristics, you may want to **emphasize one attribute** at a time on each hike, such as:

♠ flower colors and flower shapes
♠ square stems or other noticeable plant family characteristics
♠ pistil and stamen for attracting pollinators
♠ flower families
♠ opposite leaves on plants and trees
♠ tree flowers and families

❧ Your **Nature journals** could include illustrations, rubbings or pressings of the flower-of-the-week. Include a page or two for these wildflowers-of-the-week, placing them in the order they bloomed, such as May Day Flowers, Mother's Day flowers, Memorial Day flowers, Early June flowers, Solstice flowers. Give each flower a name according to its special qualities. Later, use a flower guide to identify it.

(continued)

🌲 Wildflower illustrations can be reproduced for display purposes or used as **flower identification necklaces**. To make I.D. necklaces, simply draw and color a picture of a wildflower and put its name on the back side of the necklace. Laminate your drawing with clear contact paper. Attach a string and wear it around your neck when going on wildflower hikes. You may also enjoy using wildflower illustrations that are available from your State Department of Forests and Parks, or Fish and Wildlife Department.

INDOOR SPRING WOODLAND GARDEN: A NATURE TABLE

It is not always possible to hike into the woodlands each week to enjoy the wonders of the awakening forest. In more urban settings, a nature table can provide opportunities for discovering Spring's wonders. Can you imagine a spring woodlands garden blooming right inside your home or classroom?

🌿 With a little thought and a dusting of magic, a plain table can be transformed into a beautiful garden. To begin, pass your magic wand over the table by covering it with a cloth that imitates the forest setting. What colors and textures represent spring forests? Choose some spring-colored cloths or silks to drape over a table. Add a few shelf fungi or interesting pieces of tree roots, branches, or driftwood. Fascinating stones make a nice addition to set the tone for your woodland garden.

🌿 To bring outdoor plants into an indoor **miniature woodland garden,** follow these suggestions to create a realistic, enchanting display:

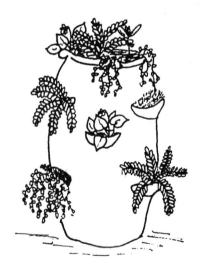

♠ **A clay strawberry pot,** with its many openings along the sides, makes a fine woodland garden planter. Plant each opening or lip with a different moss, violet, fern or trailing ground cover. However, do not take these tiny specimens from their woodland habitat unless they are growing in abundance. If possible, use forest loam in your clay strawberry pot. Otherwise, substitute moist potting soil or a germinating mix. Make sure the soil - and the clay pot - remain moist.

♠   Be sure to **dig up woodland plants** that are tiny enough that their root systems will fit easily into the small openings of the strawberry pot. One plant can be transplanted into each opening. Water thoroughly at first, drenching the soil and the pot until moisture soaks through the porous clay. There is no need to water again until the soil begins to dry.

> ☞ *Note:* Plants living in porous clay pots need more water than plants growing in plastic pots. Check your woodland friends daily to see that their thirst is satisfied and that they are becoming accustomed to their new location. Transplant again only if a plant seems poorly positioned or if it seems not to be doing well, as transplanting is stressful to the plants. To water the garden, pour water onto the soil and over the clay pot itself. Terra cotta pots may be soaked in a tub of water until thoroughly moistened. To help maintain adequate moisture levels over a weekend or during a vacation, provide a shady yet bright location for these spring wonders, for ordinarily they would receive filtered sunlight in their own home beneath the newly emerging forest canopy.

♠   An **old fish tank or fish bowl** can be adapted for woodland gardens. Place a 1/2 inch layer of charcoal on the bottom. Next, position mossy stones to create the different kinds of levels and textures you would find in the forest. Put soil between the stones, then plant tiny woodland flowers, ferns or mosses.

♠   A large, **rectangular aquarium** can be terraced so that the various levels, rising up toward the back of the tank, resemble the different levels of the forest. Transplanting directions and care are similar to those used in the strawberry pot, except that it is not necessary to immerse the terrarium in water. Daily misting will help mosses maintain moisture. If a top can be placed over the terrarium for weekends or vacations, the terrarium will remain moist enough until your return.

♠   A wonderful indoor woodland garden might consist of **a piece of interesting driftwood, a fallen tree limb or an old root stump**. Look for wood that has small nooks so you can tuck in mosses, tiny unfolding ferns or wood violets. Nooks are also good hiding places for tiny stones, crystals and tree snail shells.

❧ After tiny plants have been **transplanted** into each soil-filled nook, place your woodland garden on the nature table. Since transplanting is a serious shock for plants, it may be necessary to water and mist them on a daily basis at first. They will need extra water and loving care to help them through this difficult period. Think how you would feel if your roots were removed from the Earth! Wilting plants are a sure sign of water deprivation. Expect plants to begin responding with more vigor after a week to ten days.

❧ **Daily opportunities for discoveries** in this indoor woodland garden include:

- observing tender transplants as they gain strength and health - hooray!
- observing bud and flower formations.
- observing fern fronds uncurl to reveal their intricate delicate patterns.
- discovering miniature insect activity.
- witnessing seed formation and the release of tiny violet seeds.
- discovering flag-like spore pods waving above tiny mosses.

(continued)

Want To Do More?

- ♥ **draw and paint the mysteries** of the woodland garden, which can be kept forever in your journal.

- ♥ **delight in the changing textures and colors** of this miniature world.

- ♥ **discover the natural recycling process** of moisture and regeneration.

- ♥ **feel the joy and responsibility** of caretaking the world of nature, which will strengthen your own and nature's ability to caretake one another.

HELICOPTERS AND SNOW: SPRING SEED HIKE

How do seeds find just the right spot to grow? Spring is a wonderful time to observe trees as they pass through various stages of flower and seed production. Each has its own personality. Some trees, like the Cottonwood, blanket the earth with fluffy white seeds, which makes it seem as if Winter has returned!

🐛 On a hike, **gather seeds and observe seed production** among the forest plants. You can gather seeds from three different areas: from ground level plants, from the middle layer (bushes and shrubs), and from the uppermost layer (the trees).

🐛 Experiment with different **gathering techniques**. Which system works best for which area? Develop your own ideas for gathering, or try some of these:

♠ **Sock walks** - pull up old socks over your shoes while hiking to collect seeds that like to "hitch-hike".

♠ Bring gathering baskets or pouches for **hand-picking** seeds.

♠ Use **sweep nets**, such as butterfly nets, for gently collecting tree seeds.

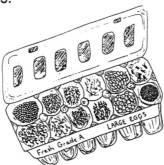

🐛 After gathering seeds from each area, you will enjoy looking at and sorting your findings. An egg carton will help you **organize the seeds**. Place each one into a separate compartment, sorting it according to its unique characteristics.

(continued)

As you closely **examine each seed**, write down questions in your nature journal. Or, answer some of these questions:

- Have you ever seen seeds like these before?
- Can you identify the parent plant that each seed came from?
- How do you think the different seeds travel from one place to another?
- Did all the plants you observed seem to be producing seeds?
- Do some seeds seem fresh and young, while others appear weathered and old? Why do you think this might be?

Illustrate spring seed-producing plants in your journal. Beside the appropriate illustration, paste or put under contact paper the seeds and pressed leaf samples you collected during your hike.

Math, Nature's Way

Play some **games** with your seeds.

- Observe them closely with a hand lens, then organize them into **symmetrical** and **asymmetrical** categories.

- Figure out how many different kinds of seeds you have, then **count** the number of seeds in each group. Next, make a **bar graph** that demonstrates the number of seeds in each group. How do your figures **compare** with your friends? Which seeds seem to be most abundant?

- **Count** seeds by 2's, 5's and 10's.

VILLAGE ON THE ROCK WALK

How can a rock show signs of Spring life? How can a rock be a home to so many forms of life? Think of all the ways this could happen, then draw your ideas in your nature journal along with any questions you may have. Finally, visit the inhabitants of a rock to find out!

🐚 Look outdoors for a rock that is covered with lichen, mosses and young plants. Examine the inhabitants of this village on the rock.

- ♠ **Lichen** looks like a flat - sometimes crusty - plant attached to a rock. Sometimes the lichen is blue-gray, sometomes yellow-green or pale green. The lichen does a giant's work, actually *crumbling* the rock! How does the lichen crack and crumble the rock? Lichen has magic substances that dissolve the rock. Over hundreds of years, lichen works with water and ice to wear away the surface of the rock. It is a very slow process, and that's one of the reasons why we treat rocks with respect. Please step gently on rocks! As you continue hiking, look for lichen on trees or rocks - they are doing the work of a giant!

- ♠ Do you see **mosses** on the rock? Much greener than lichen, mosses are rather fluffy and pillow-like, and give the rock a surprising softness. Gently feel its spongy-soft texture. Would you like to sleep on a bed of moss? Thanks to the lichen-doing-a-giant's-work, the mosses have a surface to grow on. They soak up rainwater like a sponge. After a rainy day, it is fun to feel the water in these mossy pillows.

- ♠ It is no wonder that eventually **tiny young plants** take up housekeeping among the mosses and lichen. These tiny young plants set their roots firmly into the moss. The moss holds the water for the tiny plants. If you look closely, you

might discover some of these tiny plants! Together, lichen, moss and plants help each other grow on what might otherwise be an impossible place to live.

Want To Do More?

❧ An Indoor Village on the Rock

♠ Display a small indoor "Village on a Rock" to share with those who do not have a rocky outcropping nearby to hike to. Collect mosses, rocks and miniature plants from the same habitat. Display these items on a plate or cookie sheet. Keep out of direct sunlight, mist the rock daily, and observe the miniature changes that occur on a village on a rock.

♠ Bring a bare rock indoors and sculpt some natural inhabitants out of plasticene or beeswax to live there!

♠ Create a "Village Rock" mural to hang alongside your display.

♠ When you have finished your study, carefully return the rocks, moss, and plants to their original habitat, giving thanks for the wonders that were shared.

♠ In a **Closing Share Circle**, pass around a rock with lichen growing on it and talk about the many ways Nature does a giant's work. How can we assist Nature so that the giant's work may benefit us all?

TREES IN THE BREEZE

Famous naturalist and tree lover John Muir spent many days alone in the forests of California observing trees. He had many tales to tell after walking hundreds of miles in the wilderness. On one exciting adventure, Muir observed an incredible windstorm that struck the California mountain forest. What do you think happened to the trees during this great windstorm? Do trees have different ways to survive strong winds? Listen to what John Muir discovered.

One day, John Muir was visiting a friend who lived in a cabin nestled high in a mountain valley. He said goodbye to his friend just as a violent windstorm began to sweep through the area. Unafraid, Muir was delighted by the intensity of the fierce gales. On and on he walked, fascinated by the movement, grace and flexibility of the windswept trees. He imagined the trees as dancers, moving and swirling in spiraling motions, limber and forgiving of the tearing winds. He noticed that every tree had its own unique adaptation - a shape which allowed it to move freely rather than be ripped and shredded apart by the howling winds.

And then, as though walking through the storm were not enough, Muir climbed to the top of a hundred foot spruce! Hugging it for dear life, he spent the remainder of the storm in the wildly swaying tree. He danced with the tree, feeling part of the whooshing, sweeping motions that only the trees themselves had known before. "How exhilarating," he thought, "to be part of the magical motion of dancing trees!"

Can You Sway In the Breeze?

🐝 You might like to **join some trees** in the breeze one blustery spring day. Or observe them from the safety of your home or classroom window. Watch how they sway and swoop during the oncoming storm. It's an exciting

opportunity to observe the incredible adaptations of what seem to be "rigid" trees. Observe different trees, one at a time. What do you notice about their movements?

- ♠ Do they bend, nearly touching the Earth? Do they twist?

- ♠ How do the leaves move?

- ♠ What do you notice about a tree standing alone, as opposed to trees grouped together?

- ♠ What does each tree sound like as the wind rushes through it? Does each tree sing the same wind song? Try to differentiate the songs of particular trees.

🐦 If the opportunity arises, take a hike and **visit trees after a storm** has passed. Were any of the trees damaged? Can you observe any differences between a tree that might have fallen, or one that stood strong through a storm? Try to break a dead twig and a green twig. What do you find?

🐦 **Write your own story** about an adventure with a tree.

SAVE SOME TREES FOR ME, PEOPLE

Plant some trees for the future! Both Arbor Day and Earth Day are good days for tree planting. Of course, any day is fine, as long as the Earth is warm and ready to receive trees.

"Song for the Trees"

Where would I be if there were no trees?
Where would I go to hear the breeze?
Where would I find the bees and chickadees
If suddenly the land was cleared of trees?

I like to go in where it's tall and dark
and stand where it's quiet
and listen and think.
I like to go in where it's green and deep
and sit on a log
and have a long drink.
I like to go in and pretend I'm a deer
or a mouse or a bear
or an owl living there.

Where would I be if there were no trees?
Where would I go to hear the breeze?
Where would I find the bees and chickadees
If suddenly the land was cleared of trees?

CSP

This song really makes you think, doesn't it? What do you think about using and saving trees for future generations? What can you do?

🐦 Look around your room for **"gifts from the trees"**. Identify tree products, then hang a thank you note on all their gifts.

🐦 Determine which part of the tree various products come from. The **crown of the tree** gives us fruits, nuts, seeds, shelter, leaves for compost, and drinks like cola, coffee, chocolate and coconut milk. The **trunk and sap of the tree** provide maple syrup and sugar, rubber, chewing gum, paper, bark mulch and wood for building. **Roots of a tree** give us the gifts of medicines and dyes, not to mention root beer!

🐦 **Plan a tree planting project with your family.** Plant a tree for the future! You may want to plant a tree for your mother, father, grandparents, little brother or sister. Perhaps everyone in your family or class can choose her favorite type of tree and plant it with a wish for future generations. Or plant one tree for the entire group.

🐦 **Plant a tree** in the forest, in a field, near a pond or a brook, or in a meadow-thicket. Plant one in a place that looks as if it could use a tree. Don't forget to take care of it, and visit it often! Plant one every Spring, and brighten up the planet!

Arbor Day

    ❦ Arbor Day is celebrated on different days each Spring. Check for your local Arbor day date and begin your plans for an early Spring event!   The following poem may be fun to act out on Arbor Day.

"An Arbor Day Tree"

(For four voices)

All: "Dear little tree that we plant today, what will you be when we're old and gray?"

First: "The savings bank of the squirrel and mouse, for the robin and wren an apartment house."

Second: "The dressing room of the butterfly's ball, the locust's and katydid's concert hall."

Third: "The school child's ladder in the pleasant June, the school child's tent in the July noon."

Fourth: "And my leaves shall whisper right merrily, a tale of children who planted me."

- Author Unknown

TREES OF LIFE! LUNGS OF THE PLANET

Have you ever stopped to consider and appreciate how amazing it is that trees clean and purify the Earth of dirtied air? Come along on this Guided Journey to experience the interchange of the air we all breathe - plants and animals alike.

🕊 Visit your favorite tree, or adopt any nearby tree that sparks your interest. Sit quietly beneath your tree friend, or give it a hug. Feel its rough bark against your face. Sense the strength of its trunk. Take deep slow breaths as you wonder about this. . . .

We breathe in and out all day long, but rarely are we aware of this gift of life. Take a deep breath now, focusing on what you are doing. Count to five as you fill your belly, your abdomen, and finally your chest, with air. Hold it for a second or two, then slowly release it, feeling your breath ease out from your heart center, your abdomen and your belly, up through your throat and then out your nose. Take another deep breath in the same way, counting five in, holding for two, counting five out.

"Relax, and imagine the trees breathing in your exhaled stale air and turning it into fresh oxygen. All air is recycled by trees and plants. The amount of air on the planet is always the same - it just keeps going around and around. What you breathe out, plants take in and purify. This cleansed air journeys on the winds all over the earth, giving itself to other humans and animals. Just think, someone or some animal somewhere far away may be breathing in the air you exhaled yesterday, last week, last year - or even air from the day you were born! You might be breathing the same air exhaled by a beautiful animal living in Africa or in the rain forest. You might be breathing some of the same air a climber breathed on the very top of Mt. Everest! Or you might be breathing some oxygen that Grandforest Tree made when he was just a sapling.

"Whew! Don't forget to breathe now. This time, breathe in some of that air that has journeyed across the ocean, over mountains, past forests and deserts, air that has been cleansed by some incredible tree in some magnificent part of the world. Where do you imagine the air you are breathing came from? Who, or what, do you think exhaled the air? What kind of tree might have taken in and purified the air for you? With whom or with what would you like to share your air? Imagine this for a minute and breathe. . . .

"Bring yourself back to the tree under which you are sitting. What does it feel like to breathe the very air this tree might have cleansed? Now you might like to thank the tree for this peaceful feeling. We are all cared for by Trees for Life everywhere!"

Want To Do More?

❦ We keep our homes, classrooms and work places buttoned down tight in the Winter so the heat doesn't escape. Not much fresh air gets in, and often it's pretty stale inside. No wonder we get cabin fever and look a little yellow by the time Spring gets here! **Fresh air is important to good health,** especially in the Winter. So what can we do to be sure the air inside is fresh? Plant houseplants!

♠ Certain house plants, such as Arum Ivy, Philodendron, and Spider plant, are known for their ability to purify the air. Try growing some of these inside and see if you notice a difference! By growing these "clean air machines" we can clean the stale air indoors where we live, work and play. Hooray for plants!

(continued)

❧ You may want to demonstrate how you feel about the trees that are the lungs of our planet. **Plan a community celebration** to share your appreciation and wonder about trees. Some ideas might include:

- ♠ Creating a **mural** illustrating how trees (and other green plants) recycle air.
- ♠ Performing a **skit** that shows how the air you breathe may have come from somewhere far away.
- ♠ Giving away **house plants** to elders and shut-ins who might not get out into the fresh air often.

❧ **Read, then re-tell stories** about amazing trees from around the world. Draw pictures of trees from different parts of the world, along with the people and animals they support. Some recommended stories included in the bibliography are <u>The Name of the Tree</u> and <u>Tree in the Trail</u>.

TREE DOCTORS

Did you ever wonder how a tree feels when it is healthy? The tree doctor can figure out each tree patient's general health requirements by listening to its heartbeat and checking each and every part of the tree. He can even tell how old a tree is!

First, the doctor must **locate all the parts of a tree** to be sure they are in good working order. Can you locate the bark, sap, trunk, crown, roots, leaves, fruits and seeds? Leaves, fruits and seeds may or may not be visible inevery season, depending on the species.

🐚 Where is the crown?

Where else but on the top, with all the beautiful-looking parts - **branches, twigs, leaves, flowers** and **fruit.** Check around up there, and see if there are any signs of buds, leaves, seeds or fruit. Do these tree parts look healthy? The crown is where food is made. Do you see any leaves? The leaves are the part of the crown that make the food, and are also the part of the tree that breathes.

Healthy trees bear fruit in Summer. They drop the fruit in late Fall and early Winter. Look for fruits before animals have foraged them all. In late Winter or early Spring, a healthy tree should show signs of buds. Check to see if it is breathing.

🐚 Where is the trunk?

The trunk is like a **skeleton** that holds the tree up, growing in strength and durability as the tree reaches for the sky. What is the trunk covered with? Its **bark** is like a person's skin. Is the trunk healthy? Or are there open wounds in the bark - lots of insect holes, woodpecker holes, or soft spots?

(continued)

🐛 What lies beneath the bark?

This is a mystery. It can be seen only with an X-ray machine. What do you think is under there? The **sapwood** is a highway of straw-like veins that carry sweet sap up through the tree. If you tap a sugar maple in late Winter, you can see the sap flow - help yourself to a sweet treat! Another highway of straws called **phloem** takes the food from the leaf down to the rest of the tree.

Both of these routes close down for the Winter. New layers of sapwood and phloem are laid down over the old ones, ready to carry food and water throughout the tree. These working layers are called the **cambium.**

In the very center of the tree is a heart, where its strength and beauty dwell. The **heartwood** is made up of old layers of sapwood and phloem. Listen with your ear or with a stethoscope to see if you hear a pulse. What does the heart of a tree do? What lies deep in your heart? The tree knows! Listen.

🐛 Up above and down below, check the parts that do not show.

What can you examine down there? How about looking for **roots?** Most trees keep their feet covered far below the surface, but sometimes you can find a few barefoot toes poking out. If you were a tree, you too might keep your feet well-hidden below the surface - because they would be HUGE! How big is the root system of a tree? If you don't know, just look up. That's right. The root system is similar in size and shape to the branches in the tree's crown. For an interesting close-up look at some tree feet, look for blown-down trees in the forest with their roots exposed. Wow!

The doctor can now **draw an imaginary X-ray photo** of the tree, including its earth-bound roots. How can the doctor do this? Sketch the crown and trunk of the tree. Then duplicate the crown below the ground - it's just like a reflection in a lake! Why does a tree need such big feet? Wide-spreading root-feet help anchor the tree firmly in place. The roots are also responsible for drawing water up into the tree.

(continued)

૨ When was this tree born?

The doctor needs to know this very important fact. What is your guess? Check the **height**, and maybe the **width** of the tree, for clues to its age. One sure way to tell the age of a tree is by looking at a **tree cookie,** or cross section of a tree trunk. Count the rings around the heartwood. Each ring represents a year in the life of a tree. Practice telling tree ages by counting rings on wood stumps from the wood pile. You can also make a tree cookie cross section from a tree thinning.

Another way to tell a tree's age is by looking for **bud scale scars** on the branch. Trees have their own birthday candles. Each year, as the bud casts off its hard protective scale, it leaves a scar behind. Count the scars beneath a bud case and you'll know how many candles to put on the cake. You may need to use your magnifying lens for this one!
 Happy Birthday, Dear Tree!

૨ Open wide and say Ah-h-h.

Check the ears, mouths and anything else that needs to be checked to make sure the tree is healthy. Is all in working order? Hmmmm, how do trees stay healthy?

Humans remain healthy by eating right, drinking plenty of fluids and getting enough rest. But what is the

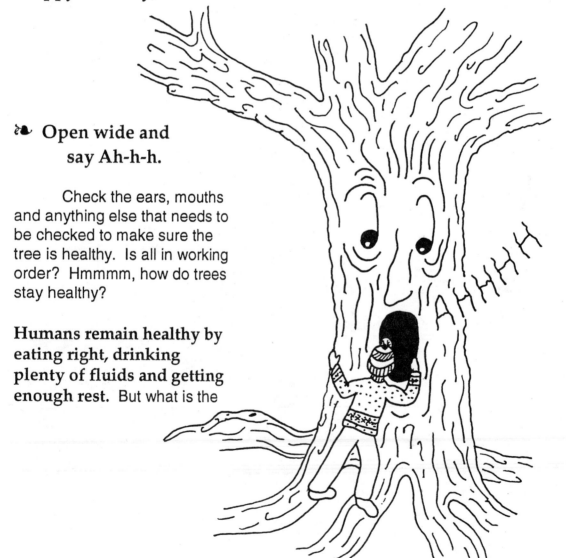

tree doctor's prescription for continued good health? Write up a "Fit for Life" Tree Plan for this tree. In your recommendations, consider sunshine, soil, water, air, dormancy (sleep), and a dose of Tender Loving Care.

Want To Do More?

❧ You can design a **tree display** on large cardboard shaped like a tree, adding details of different materials and textures. How might the parts of a tree compare to any of your own body parts, such as your skin, veins and bones?

♠ **Crown** - branches and twigs that hold leaves.

♠ **Trunk** - supports the crown, carries minerals and water up from the roots, carries food down from the leaves, and produces wood.

♠ **Roots** - support the whole tree and absorb minerals and water from the soil, as well as storing extra food through the Winter for the following year's growth.

♠ **Outer bark** - provides protection from fire, disease, and insects.

♠ **Inner bark** - sends food down to roots from the leaves.

♠ **Cambium** - the tree rings that produce inner bark and sapwood.

♠ **Sapwood** - brings minerals and water up through the trunk to the leaves.

♠ **Heartwood** - a hard inner core that provides support to the tree, though eventually these dead cells rot away.

❧ **Invite a tree surgeon** to your class for a second opinion! Ask her how trees "talk" to each other. Yes, indeed, trees communicate among themselves, especially to warn each other about insect predation.

SPRING FOREST FESTIVAL

Grandforest Tree Bids Farewell:

What a wonderful year it has been! I have enjoyed taking you on this journey through the forest. All of us who dwell among trees - living and non-living - are grateful for your friendship and your understanding. We all hope you will accept the challenge and responsibility of being Forest Caretakers. This means practicing stewardship and educating others in your community about the wonders of the woodlands. Remember - the forest is an intricate web of life that depends on all of its members to keep it in a healthy balance. Moreover, the forest does not stand in isolation from other ecosystems - forest life is woven into the fabric of all other life systems on this planet. It is not separate from the meadow-thickets, the rivers, ponds, oceans, mountains, deserts or the tropical rain forest. By taking care of the forest - by planting a single tree - you are helping to care for the Earth.

"Plan a community celebration of the Spring woodlands, and encourage everyone to take part in caring for the forest! Good luck - I hope to see you in the future!"

❧ **A Spring Woodlands Festival** can be filled with activities, displays, songs, skits, tours, and forest treats. Some suggestions follow to help you plan your festival.

- ♠ Sell **posters** that can be colored which tell about the woodland wildflowers in your area.

- ♠ Display **photographs** or **drawings** of endangered forest species.

- ♠ Display examples of **tree gifts** - products, foods, art.

♠ Perform a **puppet show or skit** based on Dr. Suess' book <u>The Lorax</u>.

♠ As a fundraiser to support local woodland wildflower programs, try **face-painting** endangered or protected flowers on friends' cheeks and foreheads.

♠ Make "Let Them Be" **T-shirts** of the woodland wildflowers you love!

♠ Teach people to create **mini-woodlands** through planting trees around their homes, neighborhoods and schools.

♠ Encourage people to set up **nature trails** for enjoying woodland trees, wildflowers and wildlife in your neighborhood or local park.

(continued)

♠ Take a **travelling Spring Woodlands show** to a nursing home so the residents can enjoy the beauty of Spring and the Forests too!

♠ Perform and teach the **poem** "Let Them Be" (page 226).

♠ Exhibit **woodland treasures.**

♠ Demonstrate a **web of forest life.**

♠ Collect and sing as many **forest songs** as you can find!

♠ Take small groups on **nature tours** of the forest.

🐌 HAPPY SPRING! 🐌

Bibliographies

Exploring the Forest with Grandforest Tree
REFERENCE BIBLIOGRAPHY

Bruchac, Joseph and Caduto, Michael, *Keeper's of the Animals*, Fulcrum Books, Golden, CO, 1991

Comstock, Anna B. *Handbook of Nature Study*, Cornell University Press, Ithaca, NY, 1974

Cornell, Joseph, *Sharing the Joys of Nature: Nature Activities for All Ages*, Dawn Publications, Nevada City, CA, 1989

Duensing, Edwar, *Talking To Fireflies, Shrinking the Moon: A Parent's Guide to Nature Activities*, A Plume Book, CA, 1990

Facklam, Margery, *Do Not Disturb: The Mysteries of Animal Hibernation and Sleep*, Sierra club, CA, 1989

Hallowell, Anne C., *Fern Finder*, Nature Study Guild, Berkely, CA, 1981

Headstrom, Richard, *Adventures with Insects*, Dover Publications, NY, 1982

Herman, Marina, *Teaching Kids to Love the Earth: Sharing A Sense of Wonder, 186 Outdoor Activities for Parents and Other Teachers*, Pfeifer-Hamilton, CA, 1991

Hunken, Jorie, *Botany for All Ages: Discovering Nature Through Activities Using Plants*, Globe Pequot, Chester, CT, 1989

Martin, Alexander, *Golden Guide to Weeds*, Golden Press, NY, NY, 1987

Merilees, Bill, *Attracting Backyard Wildlife: A Guide for Nature Lovers*, Voyageur Press, Minnesota, 1989

Parker, Arthur C., *Skunny Wundy*, George H. Doran Co., NY, NY, 1926

Seton, Ernest Thomas, *Wild Animals I Have Known*, Scribner & Sons, NY

Stokes, Donald W., *A Guide to Nature in Winter: Northeast and North Central America*, Little Brown and Co., Boston, 1976

Suzuki, David, *Looking at Insects*, Warner Books, NY, 1986

Teale, Edwin Way, *The Wilderness World of John Muir*, Houghton Mifflin, Boston, MA, 1954

Weiss, Evelyn, *Children's Songs for a Friendly Planet*, Children's Creative Response to Conflict Resolution, Nyack, NY, 1986

Zim, Herbert S., *Golden Guide to Trees*, Golden Press, NY, 1965

Zim, Herbert S., *Golden Guide to Stars*, Golden Press, NY, 1975

Zim, Herbert S., *Golden Guide to Insects*, Golden Press, NY, 1966

Zuckerman, Seth, Saving Our Ancient Forests, Living Planet Press, Venice, CA, 1991

Exploring the Forest with Grandforest Tree

RECOMMENDED CHILDREN'S LITERATURE

Arnosky, Jim, *Crinkleroot's Guide to Knowing the Trees, Macmillan Child Group, New York, NY, 1992.* Old Crinkleroot learns all there is to know by direct observation. The wonderful illustrations give you a bird's-eye view of what he sees on his adventures into the world of trees.

Baker, Jeanne, *Where the Forest Meets the Sea, Greenwillow Books, New York, NY, 1988.* The artwork in this book deserves special attention as it contains collages sculpted from clay, mosses, bark and nature's own textures. A wonderful resource for inspiring your own classroom exhibits. The story is about a father telling his son what he remembers from his own childhood wanderings when trees filled the countryside and ran down to the sea.

Beame, Rona, *Backyard Explorer Leaf and Tree Guide, Workman Publishing, New York, NY, 1989.* A fun and handy tool for starting your own leaf collection.

Brother Eagle, Sister Sky: A Message from Chief Seattle, Illustrated by Susan Jeffers, Dial Books, New York, NY, 1991. "We did not weave the web of life, we are merely a strand in it. Whatever we do to the web, we do to ourselves." Chief Seattle's moving and haunting words are accompanied by wonderful paintings of Susan Jeffers.

Bruchac, Joseph, *Faithful Hunter Abenaki Stories*, Greenfield Review Press, Greenfield Center, NY, 1988. These ancient stories remind us about our humanness, especially family values, and our need to repect the earth. Only by honoring both can we balance society's demands with life that will sustain future generations.

Cherry, Lynne, *The Great Kapok Tree: A Tale of the Amazon Rainforest, Harcourt, Brace & Janovich, San Diego, CA, 1990.* A rainforest logger sleeps beneath the kapok tree. In the sleeping man's ear, rainforest animals whisper their plea to save their home.

Dahl, Roald, *Fantastic Mr. Fox, Puffin Books, New York, NY, 1988.* This chapter book tells of the antics and adventures of several farmers who attempt to rid the chicken house of a pesty, but fantastic, Mr. Fox.

Dichn, Gwen and Terry Krautwurst, *Nature Crafts for Kids: 50 Fantastiic Things to Make with Mother Nature's Help, Sterling Lark, New York, NY, 1992.* Photos and easy instructions show how to make Pan Pipes, bug boxes, sun clocks, wildflower candles, a sawdust kiln, how to dye eggs with onion skins, make turnip lanterns, dried apples head monsters, nature kaleidosccopes, sand castles, ant houses and more!

Ehlert, Lois, *Red Leaf, Yellow Leaf, Harcourt, Brace & Janovich, 1991.* The masked secrets of leaf color are hidden in this text.

Greene, Carol, John Muir: *Man of the Wild Places,* Children's Press, Chicago, IL, 1991. The life of John Muir from boyhood describing his sensitivity and dedication toward experiencing the wild places of the world - by foot!

Holling, Clancy, *Tree in the Trail*, Houghton Mifflin, Boston, MA, 1970. A cottonwood tree lives on the Santa Fe trail for 200 years. This Medicine Tree was friend to Sioux, buffalo, and wagon train settlers.

Kervin, Rosalind, *Tree in the Moon and Other Legends of Plants and Trees, Cambridge University Press, MA, 1989.* Wonderful legends from around the world which tell the story of the trees, bushes, and the first corn.

Lane, Margaret, *The Squirrel, Dial Press, New York, NY, 1981.* This book describes some of the unseen antics of the squirrel which we might not have the good fortune to observe for ourselves.

Lerner, Carol, *A Forest Year, William Morrow, New York, NY, 1987.* Take a journey through the life of a forest year.

Lottridge, Celia Barker, *The Name of the Tree, Macmillan Publishing, New York, NY, 1989.* This Bantu folk tale tells of a great drought and of the one tree on the plain which bears the fruit to end the hunger facing all the animals. Welcome relief will come only if they can unlock the secret word to receive the tree's fruits. Great story for acting out afterward.

Mowat, Farley, *Owls in the Family, Little, Brown & Company, Boston, MA, 1962.* This chapter book describes what happens to a young boy who steals owl babies from their nest and raises them in his backyard aviary.

Pirtle, Sarah, "My Roots Go Down" from cassette *My Two Hands Hold the Earth*, Discovery Center, P.O. Box 28, Buckland, MA, 01338

Romanova, Natalia, *Once There Was a Tree, Dial Books, New York, NY, 1985.* This Soviet author traces the life story of an aging tree as it gives away of itself to passing bear, mouse, ant, and hunter. But who does the tree belong to? The tree grows from the Earth so it belongs to us all.

Rose, Deborah L., *The People Who Hugged the Trees: An Environmental Folktale, Rinehart Inc., Niwot, CO, 1990.* The ruler of the kingdom plans to clearcut the forest. In resistance to the impending destruction the villagers express their committment to the trees by hugging them, thwarting the clear-cutting efforts.

Ryder, Joan, *Chipmunk Song, Dutton, New York, NY, 1987.* Be captivated by the magic and you can feel yourself experience the life of a chipmunk!

Ryder, Joan, *Snail's Spell, Puffin, New York, NY, 1988.* Being a snail is a unique adventure you probably never thought of having - but you can with this story!

Scneiper, Claudia, *An Apple Tree through the Year, Carolrhoda Books, Minneapaolis, MN, 1987.* If there's no apple tree in your life, this book is an introduction to the seasonal rhythms of the apple.

Seuss, Dr., *The Lorax, Random Books, New York, NY, 1971.* The story of the last truffula tree seed and how it came to be.

Silverstien, Shel, *The Giving Tree, Harper & Row, New York, NY, 1964.* Stretching the span of boyhood to old age, an apple tree gives all of itself to fullfill the man's desires. This story raises questions about the balance of giving and receiving and our relationship to the natural world.

Van De Wetering, *Hugh Pine, William Morrow, New York, NY, 1992.* Chapter after chapter the author tells of the trials and tribulations of being a porcupine who lives near a main thoroughfare!

Weiss, Evelyn, *Children's Songs for a Friendly Planet,* Children's Creative Response to Conflict Resolution, Nyach, NY, 1986. Includes lyrics and music for "Under One Sky", "Let It Be", "The Earth Is My Mother", "Deep Deep", and other songs. Available from: Riverside Church, 490 Riverside Drive, NY, NY 10027

The following stories, poems, and guided journeys were written by JoAnne Dennee:

"Grandforest Tree Tells of the First Forest"
"To Be a Tree"
"Tree for Life: A Journey with Apple Tree"
"Tree for Life: A Journey with Maple"
"Tree for Life: A Journey with White Pine"
"Josie's Tree Rap Song"
"Walking with Grandforest Tree'
"Old Man Wintree"
"Winter Hush Circle Game"
"For Rent: Winter Wonderland"
"The Tree Shape Game"
The Wise Elder Trees Walk"
"Leaflets Three: Let It Be"
"Trees of Life! Lungs of the Planet"

The following stories and poems were written by Julia Hand:

"The Gift of Fire"
Haiku (pg. 81)
Cinquain (pg. 82)
"The Family of Life"
"Why Squirrel Hops Between the Trees"
"The Secret of Tree-Water"
"Let Them Be"

The following poem was written by Carolyn Peduzzi:

"Song for the Trees"

The Common Roots Program

Education So Real
You Can See It Growing.

The Food Works *Common Roots* program helps parents, teachers, and other educators develop an integrated curriculum that not only covers practical skills in science, social studies, nutrition, math, writing, and the arts, but also prepares children to confront social and environmental problems in their own communities.

Food Works is an educational organization founded in 1987 to help integrate the themes of food, ecology, and community into elementary school education.

❦ Food Works staff are available for consulting sessions and workshops with teachers, parents and community groups to help integrate the *Common Roots* program.

❦ Food Works staff can visit your group or classroom and present hands-on activities, slideshows, videos, or lectures on themes of food security, ecology, and community service learning.

❦ Food Works has developed a variety of curriculum resource materials for teachers, parents, and community members to use in the classroom. Our K-6 *Common Roots Guidebooks* are an exciting collection of hands-on, hearts-on environmental and historical activities for young learners. Now available are:

"The Wonderful World of Wigglers"	@ $14.95
"Exploring the Forest with Grandforest Tree"	@ $18.95
"Exploring the Secrets of the Meadow-Thicket"	@ $18.95
"In The Three Sisters Garden"	@ $18.95

(add $3.00 s/h per book)

For Complete information regarding the *Common Roots* program or to order additional *Common Roots Guidebooks*, write or telephone:

FOOD WORKS
64 Main Street
Montpelier, Vermont 05602
1-800-310-1515
802-223-1515